ON THE WATER

Coles at Corryvreckan

Foggy Dew R.C.C.

ON THE WATER

The Yachting Muse

Michael Gilkes

Book Guild Publishing
Sussex, England

First published in Great Britain in 2009 by
The Book Guild Ltd
Pavilion View
19 New Road
Brighton, BN1 1UF

Typesetting in Garamond by
SetSystems Ltd, Saffron Walden, Essex

Printed in Great Britain by
CPI Antony Rowe

A catalogue record for this book is
available from the British Library

ISBN 978 1 84624 314 1

CONTENTS

PREFACE

A few words as to the origin of this anthology may be in order.
About 1970, during the course of a cruise to the west coast of
Scotland and St Kilda to introduce Adlard Coles to an area to
which, in spite of his wide experience, he had never travelled,
Adlard told me that he had been invited to compile an anthology
of best sailing stories. He found himself unable to take this on and
suggested that I, with my fairly extensive yachting library, might
like to do it. This I found an interesting suggestion and proceeded
to build up a collection of fictional sailing stories which are now
presented in these pages.

We managed to arrange for permissions and appropriate fees
where necessary, and were ready to proceed to publication when
the publisher's reader, who was a pedant of pedants, started making
very considerable difficulties. For example, he decried *Three Men in
A Boat* as 'whimsy' and kept on regretting the absence of salt spray
and names such as *Slocum* and *Hiscock*. He had to be reminded that
in the original negotiations with the publishers it had been agreed
that these stories would be purely fiction. He also queried my use
of the word *gam*, a well-known whaling term, and the whole
situation was complicated by the fact that he turned out also to be
one of my patients and, as a result, medical confidentiality and
etiquette raised their heads!

It became a time of publishing recession and the publishers
decided not to continue. Nonetheless, the papers have stayed in a
briefcase all the years since and from time to time I have felt that
they are worthy of reception by a larger public – and also that it
would be nice if they were to bear the name of Adlard Coles, who

was not only a very good friend, but also a very fine character in the fields of both yachting and publishing, being the founder of the very well-known firm, Adlard Coles Limited. He acquired and edited *The Yachtsman* from 1937, wrote many books on yachting, including the definitive *Heavy Weather Sailing*, and participated in and won many ocean races, including memorable Atlantic events.

It is therefore with this in mind that I have now proceeded to publishing with the intention that this shall be in the nature of a *Festschrift* for Adlard and it gives me great pleasure to dedicate this volume to his memory. As the inscription on Shakespeare's grave at Stratford-on-Avon reminds us, 'Its one and onlie begetter'.

ACKNOWLEDGEMENTS

My thanks to the long-suffering Audrey, family,
friends and fellow members of the Royal Cruising Club,
who have for so long encouraged and endured the
activities of an 'Elephant's Child'.

Thanks are warmly tendered to the authors who agreed to the selection of their work in this volume.

Excerpt from *The Cruise of the Nona* (© Hilaire Belloc 1925) is reproduced by permission of PFD (www.pfd.co.uk) on behalf of The Estate of Hilaire Belloc.
Excerpt from *Tono-Bungay* by H G Wells is reported by permission of A P Watt Ltd on behalf of The Literary Executors of the Estate of H G Wells.
Excerpt from *Ordinary Families* by E Arnot Robertson (published by Jonathan Cape, 1933) is reproduced by permission of David Higham Associates.

Every effort has been made to trace copyright holders of material reproduced in this volume. The publishers would be pleased to hear from any we have been unable to contact.

INTRODUCTION

I well recall once hearing the heartfelt cry of the librarian of a distinguished yacht club, surveying the dusty and almost totally disregarded collection of interesting, and in many cases valuable yachting books, who exclaimed, 'Yachtsmen can't read!'

Yet, even if this be true—and there are strong grounds for suspecting it to be truer than their avid perusal of a wide variety of monthly magazines might suggest—many yachtsmen have created splendid and inspiring writing of enduring quality. Of such quantity that when faced with the task of selection there is a veritable embarrassment of riches.

As always, when faced with an impossible task of choosing 'the best' refuge has been taken in resolving only to choose from fiction, and from what may in the vernacular be classified as 'yarns'. To those who may cry, 'Where is Hiscock? Where is Coles?': nay, 'Where is Tilman?' one can only reply with H.J. Hanson (not the librarian of my opening but the begetter of the greatest of all yachting libraries—that of the Cruising Association), 'Quaff your Reynolds in the winter and go to sea in the spring.'

It has been my aim to select, from those less well-known works of fiction which not only illuminate the matter of wandering in great waters but seem to me, from personal experience, reinforced in quiet cockpit 'gams', to have played their part in my life story. How a small boy, dwelling in the Heart of England, far from coast and sea, came to attain the nirvanal state which is 'not so much an interest but more a way of life'.

There is no doubt that for a multitude the subtle magic of Kenneth Grahame has brought about the first germinal stirrings of such enlightenment. No apology is offered for opening the selection with the glorious exclamation of the Water Rat; the recall of summer days on the river. Even though not sailing it is the essence of what leads the vast majority of those who sail (and even those who dream of sailing, through books) to simply 'mess about in boats'. Every spring the sap rises, the senses reawaken. On the first balmy day the local waterside busies itself with rebirth of the endless, exquisite pleasure of again starting the cycle of the one thing in world that is truly worth doing. For the sailing man or woman the renewal comes, not at the New Year, despite even the comforts of the Boat Show, but with that first unpredictable but immortal God-given day.

It is doubtful if after *The Wind in the Willows* any other book has awakened more readers to the thrill of boats and water than *The Riddle of the Sands*. In its way this is to sailing what Jorrocks and Surtees are to hunting, Mrs Beeton to cooking, or even Halsbury to the Laws of England; but at the risk of hurt sensibilities we must surely submit that not only is it immensely more readable but can be enjoyed with only a minimal knowledge of the specialized language and instincts involved, compared with the particular argot of the hunting field. Total involvement with dinghies and just messing about in boats in a spirit of adventure is the essence of this enduring work.

How many of those cranially slightly thinning, portly figures are daily acting out Mittyesque fantasies derived from memories of the epic row of Davies and Carruthers? I dare you to arrive with them at journeys end without a feeling of excitement, exhaustion and achievement.

Hilaire Belloc is too often consigned to posterity as a faded *littérateur*, suspect because of his foreign association: Chestertonian but lacking the Chesterton graces of compassion, humour and paradox. Yet those who sailed with Belloc are not long departed and testify that in *The Cruise of the Nona* he distilled all the essence and spirit of boats and sailing. This is a book which I found as I came of age. I am sure that for others it too can serve as a fixative of as yet unseen images imprinted by early experience.

It is not so very long ago that a no doubt otherwise repectable, and perhaps even intelligent person with some pretensions to wisdom, dismissed *Three Men in a Boat* as 'whimsy'. It is doubtful if such a one would be allowed in Davy Jones' locker and would surely have been consigned by Dante to the nethermost circles of Hell.

Perhaps you have forgotten the immortality of this work. Perhaps until this day you were unaware of its existence. What is certain is that in this episode it is sailing and I think it likely that it will make you laugh. Story it may be but, like all good stories, illuminates daily and recurrent truth.

I have often been asked by the unenlightened (and by now you will appreciate that means anyone for whom water and boats are not something special) whether my wife and/or family/children/ dog/parrot (a) enjoy sailing, (b) go sailing with me, (c) mind if I go sailing without them (this latter shows some appreciation of the true situation). By such I am constantly reminded of the percipient novel *Ordinary Families* by E. Arnot Robertson. The eleven-year old heroine delicately and subtly recounts her steady conversion to a yacht and boat hater as a consequence of the relentless and fanatical boat-madness of her delightful, well-meaning but somewhat insensitive father.

For those who may conjecture how best to inculcate in a reluctant wife and growing family their own obsession with nautical affairs the long extract that I have selected cannot be bettered as a dire, solemn and gripping warning. I doubt if there is a more poignant moment in the entire literature of sailing than the final cry.

As Solomon knew, the ways of a ship with the sea are indeed infinite and not to be known, but John Scott Hughes, for many years Yachting Correspondent for *The Times* served a long and comprehensive apprenticeship. His piece epitomises yet another aspect of sailing. The anxiety of fog and poor visibility even in quite familiar and parochial surroundings. Not only does it convey this but, at the risk of further hurting susceptibilities I have become certain over the years, of the general truth of the observation with which his tale opens.

Indeed, the sea engenders truth and when sailing one is often, though sometimes reluctantly, offered it face to face. One such truth has been expressed by a greater mind than mine: 'Man is the Questing Beast, Woman the Nesting Beast.' Even the archetype of all pelagic birds, the Wandering Albatross must retire to the rock and tussock of South Georgia and the Sub-Antarctic Islands to do its mating; and women do successfully nest at sea. It would be more than simple neglect if one had not, by this stage, chosen a story relating to the activities at sea of at least one half of humanity. While I know little of Kay Cartwright, I am in no doubt that she knows what she is talking about, both with regard to her own sex and to the things which arise between men, women and boats. I am sure that this is only a story but, as with all good ones, it carries a ring of veracity.

For yachtsmen the name of Alf Loomis, one of the most delightful of Revolting Colonists, is synonymous with the growth, history and recording of the peculiar activity known as Ocean Racing. This has been likened to standing under an ice-cold shower tearing up five pound notes, or it may be hundred dollar bills. Less well-known on this side of the Atlantic is his awful and fictional, but no less real and internationally recognisable, group, 'The Lee Rail Vikings'. Their total vileness not only excels the liveliest inventions of Stephen Potter's Lifemanship but epitomises the readiness of man to inflict his more unpleasant activities on even the awesome and truth-compelling environment of the sea.

The real father figure of yachting and small boat sailing, though it will be a name known only to a few, was R.T. McMullen, a Victorian stockbroker. In mid-century he finally became so disenchanted with the indolence and incompetence of his paid hands that one day in Cherbourg he dismissed them and sailed home to

4

the Thames single-handed. This in a yacht significantly larger than the majority of those we might encounter today. Having once achieved independence he never looked back. His end—discovered by French fishermen, over the Hurd Deep—at the helm of his *Perseus*—was little different from that of Alf Loomis' hero. When the time is due and the tide runs out there will be many who would echo his final hope.

Considerable restraint was required not to quote Alf Loomis on Ocean Racing. It would be peverse, particularly in the modern context of sailing not to select an extract redolent of this activity. J.D. Sleightholme, sometime Editor of *Yachting Monthly*, for many years delighted his readers with his anecdotal genius. 'They Walk by Night' is fictional, at least one would hope so, bearing in mind the final episode. Although the story is not specifically about Ocean Racing its evocation of the atmosphere and interaction on board an offshore racing yacht at night is totally authentic. Even Alf Loomis never more accurately portrayed what it is that by some peculiar quirk of peversity incites men (and women) to return to its clutches again and again.

Weston Martyr was a journalist as well as a yachtsman, and may be revered as one of the founding fathers of the Ocean Racing Club. Although it did not invent this peculiar activity it was a prime mover in its genesis and growth. Author of a famous story, *The £200 Millionaire*, in 'Smith versus Lichtensteiger' he relates a tale with genuine yachting verity; it is also an engrossing story. Let me say nothing which might dilute the spell.

I do know the identity of K. Humphrey Shakewell, the pseudonym of a gifted artist, distantly related to a famous explorer and for many years renowned as the 'Chairman of the Racing Dinghy Crews Union'. His description of *A Nice Day at Willow Reach* catches to perfection the atmosphere of one of our senior dinghy-racing clubs. It is also an ideal piece to fill a yawning gap in the overall sailing scene of this selection. It is the racing of small boats and dinghies that has brought so many to an escapist activity which can replace the *Sturm und Drang* of daily routine. It should be emphasized that the bonds of brotherhood between fisherman and dinghy sailors, (particularly those of inland waters, although the denizens of harbour walls are not to be neglected in this context) are certainly as firm and loving as those delineated here. International Hepplewhites are those superb examples of boat craftmanship, the International 14ft Dinghies. Not only are they the hardest of craft to sail, if one is to avoid being drummed out of the class, but their maintenance is on a par with that of a concert grand piano.

No apology is due if many of the stories herein have an Anglo-Saxon or even English bias. Charles II's yacht, which started it all, came from Holland. But the growth of yachting over the last 150 years has, until quite recently, been largely an English activity (with, of course, prominent Scots, Irish and Welsh overtones). The myriad of sailors, longshoremen and associated characters who peopled our coasts with bawleys and trawlers, quay punts and hog-boats linger on in every converted lifeboat and clumbungay (though in devastatingly diminished numbers) that ventures its bow past the harbour head on a calm summer Sunday.

This aspect of the yachting scene, is depicted in A.E. Copping's tales of *Gotty* (and the Guv'nor) and particularly in *In Furrin Parts*. Copies of these stories are of such rarity—as are those of William Hope Hodgson (another Edwardian figure for whom unfortunately there is no room here)—that I myself have never seen the original volumes and only encountered them reprinted in the more enlightened yachting press.

Copping's creations are characters bred by the sea faithfully observed. If the fare so far placed before you has not inculcated a fascinated horror akin to that of a bird confronted by a snake, I would hope that this one should do the trick and that you will soon be on the way *To be Gone for a Seaman*.

The author of the next piece is unknown to me but it appeared in one of the great organs of yachting literature, the *Journal of the Clyde Cruising Club*, the others being the *Journal of the Royal Cruising Club* (available to the public as *Roving Commissions*), the *Bulletin of the Cruising Association* and the occasional publications of the Cruising Club of America.

So far missing from this collection is a sense of the supernatural and eerie which is inseparable at times from 'business in great waters'. As a confirmed sceptic and non-UFO believer I still have no explanation for the occasion one fine evening in the Gulf Stream waters of the Atlantic when all five of us observed an inexplicable light moving across the heavens. We solemnly entered in the log our firm conviction that we could come to no rational explanation for the phenomonen which we had observed.

Of a slightly different order *A Night in the Treshnish Islands* evokes the spirit of that master mariner, Captain Joshua Slocum, who must remain the *primus inter pares* of those who have sailed alone around the world. Here is the sense of the inexplicable, even in familiar surroundings, so often the lot of those who go to sea.

I seek no forgiveness for remaining on the West Coast of Scotland with my penultimate choice. Although, with Socrates, I find myself increasingly certain of what I do not know, yet of one thing I remain certain: that quite the most beautiful place anywhere on the Earth's surface is there. And amongst its myriad bays, islands and shores there is none so mysterious, awe inspiring or compelling as the remarkable network of straits and inlets in the Sounds of Jura and Scarba known as the Gulf of Corryvreckan and the Race of the Grey Dogs. I freely admit to having over the years acquired an increasing fascination not just with the way of ships with the sea but with the moods of the sea itself in the form of tide rips, currents, races and the infinite variety of effects of wind on waves and water.

I have never seen the Straits of Messina, the other archetypal whirlpool—and of course *The Maelstrom*, though based on a genuine Norwegian phenomonen, is merely fiction. But we need not bother with Poe when we face W.H. Murray's Scots-based *Maelstrom*, an irresistible combination of thriller with the powerful and over-whelming fascination of the Gulf itself. Distinguished by his mountaineering record as well as his readable and knowledgeable guides to Scots topography, he has studied the Coirebreachan in its infinite variety of mood. In this piece you will find the full spirit of the great Atlantic flood tide, running apparently the wrong way, forced up from 80 to 20 fathoms, rearing up by the constriction of a strait less than half a mile wide. So doing it meets the full force of the Atlantic swell pounding on the western shores of Jura and Scarba. Even on a calm day there is an impression of natural forces of an almost nuclear character. When the wind is fierce from the West the turmoil is beyond description. Murray has very nearly achieved the impossible task of describing the indescribable.

I make no apology for closing with a piece not strictly yachting. But a claim to have taken the first private vessel down the Thames to Sea Reach in October 1945 with the peacetime lifting of restrictions justifies the inclusion of the final pages of H.G. Wells' finest novel *Tono-Bungay*. The hero, having survived the catastrophes engendered by his picaresque Uncle Ponderevo, sets forth on a new life and venture on the bridge of his new destroyer, just launched at Chiswick. His progess through the gathering dusk epitomizes the emotions which every sailing man and woman may experience at some time—if they are lucky on more that one occasion—as they press downriver, leaving the city lights behind, into the ever familiar yet eternally awesome darkness, beyond which lies another day and other seas.

These things have pleased me. I hope they will give pleasure to you.

THE WIND IN THE WILLOWS

Kenneth Grahame

The river glideth at his own sweet will;
Dear God! The very houses seem asleep;
And all that mighty heart is lying still!

The River Bank

The Mole had been working very hard all the morning, spring-cleaning his little home. First with brooms, then with dusters; then on ladders and steps and chairs, with a brush and a pail of whitewash; till he had dust in his throat and eyes, and splashes of whitewash, all over his black fur, and an aching back and weary arms. Spring was moving in the air above and in the earth below and around him, penetrating even his dark and lowly little house with its spirit of divine discontent and longing. It was small wonder, then, that he suddenly flung down his brush on the floor, said 'Bother!' and 'O blow!' and also 'Hang spring-cleaning!' and bolted out of the house without even waiting to put on his coat. Something up above was calling him imperiously, and he made for the steep little tunnel which answered in his case to the gravelled carriage-drive owned by animals whose residences are nearer to the sun and air. So he scraped and scratched and scrabbled and scrooged, and then he scrooged again and scrabbled and scratched and scraped, working busily with his little paws and muttering to himself, 'Up we go! Up we go!' till at last, pop! his snout came out into the sunlight, and he found himself rolling in the warm grass of a great meadow.

'This is fine!' he said to himself. 'This is better than whitewashing!' The sunshine struck hot on his fur, soft breezes caressed his heated brow, and after the seclusion of the cellarage he had lived in so long the carol of happy birds fell on his dulled hearing almost like a shout. Jumping off all his four legs at once, in the joy of living and the delight of spring witaout its cleaning, he pursued his way across the meadow till he reached the hedge on the further side.

'Hold up!' said an elderly rabbit at the gap. 'Sixpence for the privilege of passing by the private road!' He was bowled over in an instant by the impatient and contemptuous Mole, who trotted along the side of the hedge chaffing the other rabbits as they peeped hurriedly from their holes to see what the row was about, 'Onion-sauce! Onion-sauce!' he remarked jeeringly, and was gone before they could think of a thoroughly satisfactory reply. Then they all started grumbling at each other. 'How *stupid* you are! Why didn't you tell him—' 'Well, why didn't *you* say—' 'You might have reminded him—' and so on, in the usual way; but, of course, it was then much too late, as is always the case.

It all seemed too good to be true. Hither and thither through the meadows he rambled busily, along the hedgerows, across the copses, finding everywhere birds building, flowers budding, leaves thrusting—everything happy, and progressive, and occupied. And instead of having an uneasy conscience pricking him and whispering 'Whitewash!' he somehow could only feel how jolly it was to be the only idle dog among all these busy citizens. After all, the best part of a holiday is perhaps not so much to be resting yourself, as to see all the other fellows busy working.

He thought his happiness was complete when, as he meandered aimlessly along, suddenly he stood by the edge of a full-fed river. Never in his life had he seen a river before—this sleek, sinuous, full-bodied animal, chasing and chuckling, gripping things with a gurgle and leaving them with a laugh, to fling itself on fresh playmates that shook themselves free, and were caught and held again. All was a-shake and a-shiver—glints and gleams and spar-kles, rustle and swirl, chatter and bubble. The Mole was bewitched, entranced, fascinated. By the side of the river he trotted as one trots, when very small, by the side of a man, who holds one spellbound by exciting stories; and when tired at last, he sat on the bank, while the river still chattered on to him, a babbling proces-sion of the best stories in the world, sent from the heart of the earth to be told at last to the insatiable sea.

As he sat on the grass and looked across the river, a dark hole in the bank opposite, just above the water's edge, caught his eye, and dreamily he fell to considering what a nice snug dwelling-place it would make for an animal with a few wants and fond of a bijou riverside residence, above flood-level and remote from noise and dust. As he gazed, something bright and small seemed to twinkle down in the heart of it, vanished, then twinkled once more like a tiny star. But it could hardly be a star in such an unlikely situation; and it was too glittering and small for a glow-worm Then, as he looked, it winked at him, and so declared itself to be an eye; and a small face began gradually to grow up round it, like a frame round a picture.

A brown little face, with whiskers.

A grave round face, with the same twinkle in its eye that had first attracted his notice.

Small neat ears and thick silky hair.

It was the Water Rat!

Then the two animals stood and regarded each other cautiously.

'Hullo, Mole!' said the Water Rat.

'Hullo, Rat!' said the Mole.

'Would you like to come over?' inquired the Rat presently.

'Oh, it's all very well to *talk*,' said the Mole, rather pettishly, he being new to a river and riverside life and its ways.

The Rat said nothing, but stooped and unfastened a rope and hauled on it; then lightly stepped into a little boat which the Mole had not observed. It was painted blue outside and white within, and was just the size for two animals; and the Mole's whole heart went out to it at once, even though he did not yet fully understand its uses.

The Rat sculled smartly across and made fast. Then he held up his fore-paw as the Mole stepped gingerly down. 'Lean on that!' he said. 'Now then, step lively!' and the Mole to his surprise and rapture found himself actually seated in the stern of a real boat.

'This has been a wonderful day!' said he, as the Rat shoved off and took to the sculls again. 'Do you know, I've never been in a boat before in all my life.'

'What?' cried the Rat, open-mouthed. 'Never been in a—you never—well, I—what have you been doing, then?'

'Is it so nice as all that?' asked the Mole shyly, though he was quite prepared to believe it as he leant back in his seat and surveyed the cushions, the oars, the rowlocks, and all the fascinating fittings, and felt the boat sway lightly under him.

'Nice? It's the *only* thing,' said the Water Rat solemnly, as he leant forward for his stroke. 'Believe me, my young friend, there is *nothing*—absolutely nothing—half so much worth doing as simply messing about in boats. Simply messing,' he went on dreamily: 'messing—about—in—boats; messing—'

'Look ahead, Rat!' cried the Mole suddenly.

It was too late. The boat struck the bank full tilt. The dreamer, the joyous oarsman, lay on his back at the bottom of the boat, his heels in the air.

'—about in boats—or *with* boats,' the Rat went on composedly, picking himself up with a pleasant laugh. 'In or out of 'em, it doesn't matter. Nothing seems really to matter, that's the charm of it. Whether you get away, or whether you don't; whether you arrive at your destination or whether you reach somewhere else, or whether you never get anywhere at all, you're always busy, and you never do anything in particular; and when you've done it there's always something else to do, and you can do it if you like, but you'd much better not. Look here! If you've really nothing else on hand this morning, supposing we drop down the river together, and have a long day of it?'

The Mole waggled his toes from sheer happiness, spread his chest with a sigh of full contentment, and leaned back blissfully into the soft cushions. '*What* a day I'm having!' he said. 'Let us start at once!'

THE RIDDLE OF THE SANDS

Erskine Childers

Blindfold to Memmert

'Here she comes,' said Davies. It was nine o'clock on the next day, October 22, and we were on deck waiting for the arrival of the steamer from Norddeich. There was no change in the weather— still the same stringent cold, with a high barometer, and only fickle flaws of air; but the morning was gloriously clear, except for a wreath or two of mist curling like smoke from the sea, and an attenuated belt of opaque fog on the northern horizon. The harbour lay open before us, and very commodious and civilized it looked enclosed between two long piers which ran quite half a mile out from the land to the roadstead (Riff-Gat, by name) where we lay. A stranger might have taken it for a deep and spacious haven; but this of course was an illusion, due to the high water. Davies knew that three-quarters of it was mud, the remainder being a dredged-out channel along the western pier. A couple of tugs, a dredger, and a ferry packet with steam up, were moored on that side, a small stack of galliots on the other. Beyond these was another vessel, a galliot in build, but radiant as a queen among sluts; her varnished sides and spars flashing orange in the sun. These and her snow-white sail-covers and the twinkle of brass and gun-metal, proclaimed her to be a yacht, I had already studied her through the glasses and read on her stern *Medusa*. A couple of sailors were swabbing her decks; you could hear the sluish of the water and the scratching of deck-brooms. '*They* can see us anyway,' Davies had said.

15

For that matter all the world could see us—certainly the incoming steamer must; for we lay as near to the pier as safety permitted, abreast of the berth she would occupy, as we knew by a gangway and a knot of sailors.

A packet boat, not bigger than a big tug, was approaching from the south.

'Remember, we're not supposed to know he's coming,' I said; 'let's go below.' Besides the skylight, our 'coachhouse' cabin top had little oblong side windows. We wiped clean those on the port side and watched events from them, kneeling on the sofa.

The steamer backed her paddles, flinging out a wash that set us rolling to our scuppers. There seemed to be very few passengers aboard, but all of them were gazing at the *Dulcibella* while the packet was warped alongside. On the forward deck there were some market-women with baskets, a postman, and a weedy youth who might be an hotel-waiter; on the after-deck, standing close together, were two men in ulsters and soft felt hats.

'There he is!' said Davies, in a tense whisper, 'the tall one.' But the tall one turned abruptly as Davies spoke and strode away behind the deck-house, leaving me just a lightning impression of a grey beard and a steep tanned forehead, behind a cloud of cigar-smoke. It was perverse of me, but, to tell the truth, I hardly missed him, so occupied was I by the short one, who remained leaning on the rail, thoughtfully contemplating the *Dulcibella* through gold-rimmed pince-nez: a sallow, wizened old fellow, beetle-browed, with a bush of grizzled moustache and a jet-black tuft of beard on his chin. The most remarkable feature was the nose, which was broad and flat, merging almost imperceptibly in the wrinkled cheeks. Lightly beaked at the nether extremity, it drooped towards an enormous cigar which was pointing at us like a gun just discharged. He looked wise as Satan, and you would say he was smiling inwardly.

'Who's that?' I whispered to Davies.

(There was no need to talk in whispers, but we did so instinctively.)

16

'Can't think,' said Davies. 'Hullo! she's backing off, and they've not landed.'

Some parcels and mail-bags had been thrown up, and the weedy waiter and two market-women had gone up the gangway, which was now being hauled up, and were standing on the quay. I think one or two other persons had first come aboard unnoticed by us, but at the last moment a man we had not seen before jumped down to the forward deck. 'Grimm!' we both ejaculated at once.

The steamer whistled sharply, circled backwards into the roadstead, and then steamed away. The pier soon hid her, but her smoke showed she was steering towards the North Sea.

'What does this mean?' I asked.

'There must be some other quay to stop at nearer the town,' said Davies. 'Let's go ashore and get your letters.'

We had made a long and painful toilette that morning, and felt quite shy of one another as we sculled towards the pier, in much-creased blue suits, conventional collars, and brown boots. It was the first time for two years that I had seen Davies in anything approaching a respectable garb; but a fashionable watering-place, even in the dead season, exacts respect; and, besides, we had friends to visit.

We tied up the dinghy to an iron ladder, and on the pier found our inquisitor of the night before smoking in the doorway of a shed marked 'Harbour-Master'. After some civilities we inquired about the steamer. The answer was that it was a Saturday, and she had therefore gone on to Juist. Did we want a good hotel? The 'Vier Jahreszeiten' was still open, etc.

'Juist, by Jove!' said Davies, as we walked on. 'Why are those three going to Juist?'

'I should have thought it was pretty clear. They're on their way to Memmert.'

Davies agreed, and we both looked longingly westward at a straw-coloured streak on the sea.

'Is it some meeting, do you think?' said Davies.

17

'Looks like it. We shall probably find the *Kormoran* here, windbound.'

And find her we did soon after, the outermost of the stack of galliots, on the further side of the harbour. Two men, whose faces we took a good look at, were sitting on her hatch, mending a sail.

Flooded with sun, yet still as the grave, the town was like a dead butterfly for whom the healing rays had come too late. We crossed some deserted public gardens commanded by a gorgeous casino, its porticos heaped with chairs and tables; so past kiosques and cafés, great white hotels with boarded windows, bazaars and booths, and all the stale lees of vulgar frivolity, to the post office, which at least was alive. I received a packet of letters and purchased a local timetable from which we learnt that the steamer sailed daily to Borkum via Norderney, touching three times a week at Juist (weather permitting). On the return journey today it was due at Norderney at 7.30 p.m. Then I inquired the way to the 'Vier Jahreszeiten', 'for whatever your principles, Davies,' I said, 'we are going to have the best breakfast money can buy! We've got the whole day before us.'

The 'Four Seasons' hotel was on the esplanade facing the northern beach. Living up to its name, it announced on an illuminated signboard, 'inclusive terms for winter visitors, special attention to invalids, etc.' Here in a great glass restaurant, with the unruffled blue of ocean spread out before us, we ate the king of breakfasts, dismissed the waiter, and over long and fragrant Havanas examined my mail at leisure.

'What a waste of good diplomacy!' was my first thought; for nothing had been tampered with, so far as we could judge from the minutest scrutiny, directed, of course, in particular to the two franked official letters (for to my surprise there were two) from Whitehall.

'The first in order of date (October 6) ran—'Dear Carruthers, take another week by all means.—Yours, etc.'

The second (marked 'urgent') had been sent to my home address and forwarded. It was dated October 15, and cancelled the previous letter, requesting me to return te London without delay—'I am sorry to abridge your holiday, but we are very busy, and, at present, short-handed.—Yours, etc.' There was a dry postscript to the effect that another time I was to be good enough to leave more regular and definite information as to my whereabouts when absent.

'I'm afraid I never got this,' I said, handing it to Davies.

'You won't go, will you?' said he, looking, nevertheless, with unconcealed awe at the great man's handwriting under the haughty official crest. Meanwhile I discovered an endorsement on a corner of the envelope—'Don't worry, it's only the Chief's fuss. M__' I promptly tore up the envelope. There are domestic mysteries which it would be indecent and disloyal to reveal, even to one's best friend. The rest of my letters need no remark; I smiled over some and blushed over others—all were voices from a life which was infinitely far away. Davies, meanwhile, was deep in the foreign intelligence of a newspaper, spelling it out line by line, and referring impatiently to me for the meaning of words.

'Hullo!' he said suddenly, 'same old game! Hear that siren?'

A curtain of fog had grown on the northern horizon and was drawing shorewards slowly but surely.

'It doesn't matter, does it?' I said.

'Well, we must get back to the yacht. We can't leave her alone in a fog.'

There was some marketing to be done on the way back, and in the course of looking for the shops we wanted we came on the Schwannallee and noted its position. Before we reached the harbour the fog was on us, charging up the streets in dense masses. Happily a tram-line led right up to the pier-head, or we should have lost our way and wasted time which, in the event, was of priceless value. Presently we stumbled up against the Harbour Office, which was our landmark for the steps where we had tied up the dinghy. The same official appeared and good-naturedly held the painter while we handed in our parcels. He wanted to know why we had left the flesh-pots of the 'Vier Jahreszeiten'. To look after our yacht, of course. There was no need, he objected; there would be no traffic moving while the fog lasted, and the fog, having come on at that hour, had come to stay. If it did clear he would keep an eye on the yacht for us. We thanked him, but thought we would go aboard.

'You'll have a job to find her now,' he said.

The distance was eighty yards at the most, but we had to use a scientific method, the same one in fact that Davies had used last night in the approach to the eastern pier.

'Row, straight out at right angles to the pier,' he said now; I did so, Davies sounding with his scull between the strokes. He found the bottom after twenty yards, that being the width of the dredged-out channel at this point. Then we turned to the right and moved gently forward, keeping touch with the edge of the mud-bank (for all the world like blind men tapping along a curbstone) and taking short excursions from it, till the *Dulcibella* hove in view.

'That's partly luck,' Davies commented; 'we ought to have had a compass as well.'

We exchanged shouts with the man on the pier to show we had arrived.

'It's very good practice, that sort of thing,' said Davies, when we had disembarked.

'You've got a sixth sense,' I observed. 'How far could you go like that?'

'Don't know. Let's have another try. I can't sit still all day. Let's explore this channel.'

'*Why not go to Memmert?*' I said in fun.

'To Memmert?' said Davies slowly; 'by Jove, that's an idea!'

'Good heavens, man! I was joking. Why, it's ten mortal miles.'

'More,' said Davies absently, 'It's not so much the distance—what's the time? Ten-fifteen: quarter ebb—What am I talking about? We made our plans last night.'

But seeing him, to my amazement, serious, I was stung by the splendour of the idea I had awakened. Confidence in his skill was second nature to me. I swept straight on to the logic of the thing, the greatness, the completeness of the opportunity, if by a miracle it could be seized and used. Something was going on at Memmert to-day: our men had gone there; here were we, ten miles away, in a smothering, blinding fog. It was known we were here—Dollmann and Grimm knew it; the crew of the *Medusa* knew it; the crew of the *Kormoran* knew it; the man on the pier, whether he cared or not, knew it. But none of them knew Davies as I knew him. Would anyone dream for an instant—?

'Stop a second,' said Davies, 'give me two minutes.' He whipped out the German chart. 'Where exactly should we go?' ('Exactly'! The word tickled me hugely.)

'To the depot, of course; it's our only chance.'

'Listen, then—there are two routes: the outside one, by the open sea, right round Juist, and doubling south*—the simplest, but the longest; the depot's at the south point of Memmert, and Memmert's nearly two miles long.'

'How far would that way be?'

'Sixteen miles good. And we should have to row in a breaking swell most of the way, close to land.'

'Out of the question; it's too public, too, if it clears. The steamer went that way and will come back that way. We must go inside over the sands. Am I dreaming, though? Can you possibly find the way?'

'I shouldn't wonder. But I don't believe you see the hitch. It's the *time* and the falling tide. High water was about 8.15: it's now 10.15, and all those sands are drying off. We must cross the See-Gat and strike that boomed channel, the Memmert Balje, strike it, freeze on to it—can't cut off an inch—and pass that 'watershed' you see there before it's too late. It's an infernally bad one, I can see. Not even a dinghy will cross it for an hour each side of low water.'

'Well, how far is the "watershed"?'

'Good Lord! What are we talking for? Change, man, change! Talk while we're changing.' (He began flinging off his shore-clothes, and I did the same.) 'It's at least five miles to the end of it,

* See Chart B

21

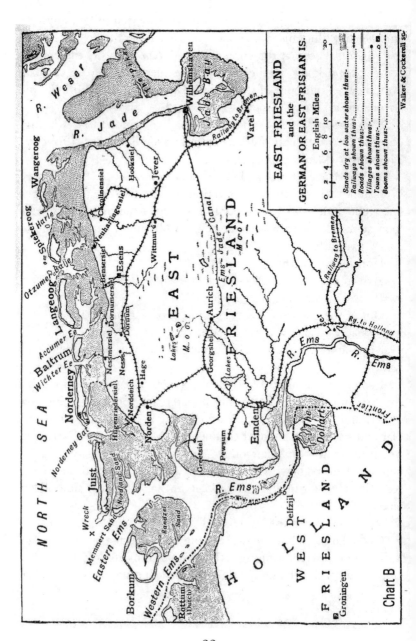

six, allowing for bends; hour and a half hard pulling; two allowing for checks. Are you fit? You'll have to pull the most. Then there are six or seven more miles—easier ones. And then—What are we to do when we get there?'

'Leave that to me,' I said. 'You get me there.'

'Supposing it clears?'

'After we get there? Bad; but we must risk that. If it clears on the way there it doesn't matter by this route; we shall be miles from land.'

'What about getting back?'

'We shall have a rising tide, anyway. If the fog lasts—can you manage in fog *and* dark?'

'The dark makes it no more difficult, if we've a light to see the compass and chart by. You trim the binnacle-lamp—no, the riding-light. Now give me the scissors, and don't speak a word for ten minutes. Meanwhile, think it out, and load the dinghy—(by Jove! though, don't make a sound)—some grub and whisky, the boat-compass, lead, riding-light, matches, *small* boathook, grapnel and line.'

'Foghorn?'

'Yes, and the whistle too.'

'A gun?'

'What for?'

'We're after ducks.'

'All right. And muffle the rowlocks with cotton-waste.'

I left Davies absorbed in the charts, and softly went about my own functions. In ten minutes he was on the ladder, beckoning.

'I've done,' he whispered. 'Now *shall* we go?'

'I've thought it out. Yes,' I answered.

This was only roughly true, for I could not have stated in words all the pros and cons that I had balanced. It was an impulse that drove me forward; but an impulse founded on reason, with just a tinge, perhaps, of superstition; for the quest had begun in a fog and might fitly end in one.

It was twenty-five minutes to eleven when we noiselessly pushed

23

off. 'Let her drift,' whispered Davies, 'the ebb'll carry her past the pier.'

We slid by the *Dulcibella*, and she disappeared. Then we sat without speech or movement for about five minutes, while the gurgle of tide through piles approached and passed. The dinghy appeared to be motionless, just as a balloon in the clouds may appear to its occupants to be motionless, though urged by a current of air. In reality we were driving out of the Riff-Gat into the See-Gat. The dinghy swayed to a light swell.

'Now pull,' said Davies, under his breath; 'keep it long and steady, above all, steady—both arms with equal force.'

I was on the bow-thwart; he *vis-à-vis* to me on the stern seat, his left hand behind him on the tiller, his right forefinger on a small square of paper which lay on his knees; this was a section cut out from the big German chart (Chart B). On the midship-thwart between us lay the compass and a watch. Between these three objects—compass, watch, and chart—his eyes darted constantly, never looking up or out, save occasionally for a sharp glance over the side at the flying bubbles, to see that I was sustaining a regular speed. My duty was to be his automaton, the human equivalent of a marine engine whose revolutions can be counted and used as data by the navigator. My arms must be regular as twin pistons; the energy that drove then as controllable as steam. It was a hard ideal to reach, for the complex mortal tends to rely on all the senses God has given him, so unfitting himself for mechanical exactitude when a sense (eyesight, in my case) fails him. At first it was constantly 'left' or 'right' from Davies, accompanied by a bubbling from the rudder.

'This won't do, too much helm,' said Davies, without looking up. 'Keep your stroke, but listen to me. Can you see the compass card?'

'When I come forward.'

'Take your time, and don't get flurried, but each time you come forward have a good look at it. The course is sou'-west half-west. You take the opposite, north-east half-east, and keep her *stern* on

24

that. It'll be rough, but it'll save some helm, and give me a hand free if I want it.'

I did as he said, not without effort, and our progress gradually became smoother, till he had no need to speak at all. The only sound now was one like the gentle simmer of a saucepan away to port—the lisp of surf I knew it to be—and the muffled grunt of the rowlocks. I broke the silence once to say, 'It's very shallow.' I had touched sand with my right scull.

'Don't talk,' said Davies.

About half an hour passed, and then he added sounding to his other occupations. 'Plump' went the lead at regular intervals, and he steered with his hip while pulling in the line. Very little of it went out at first, then less still. Again I struck bottom, and glancing aside saw weeds. Suddenly he got a deep cast, and the dinghy, freed, from the slight drag which shallow water always inflicts on a small boat, leapt buoyantly forward. At the same time, I knew by boils on the smooth surface that we were in a strong tide-way.

'The Buse Tief,'* muttered Davies. 'Row hard now, and steady as a clock.'

For a hundred yards or more I bent to my sculls and made her fly. Davie's was getting six-fathom casts, till, just as suddenly as it had deepened, the water shoaled—ten feet, six, three, one—the dinghy grounded.

'Good!' said Davies. 'Back her off! Pull your right only.' The dinghy spun round with her bow to NNW. 'Both arms together! Don't you worry about the compass now; just pull, and listen for orders. There's a tricky bit coming.'

He put aside the chart, kicked the lead under the seat, and, kneeling on the dripping coils of line, sounded continuously with the butt-end of the boathook, a stumpy little implement, notched at intervals of a foot, and often before used for the same purpose. All at once I was aware that a check had come, for the dinghy swerved and doubled like a hound ranging after scent.

* See Chart B

'Stop her,' he said suddenly, 'and throw out the grapnel.'

I obeyed and we brought up, swinging to a slight current, whose direction Davies verified by the compass. Then for half a minute he gave himself up to concentrated thought. What struck me most about him was that he never for a moment strained his eyes through the fog; a useless exercise (for five yards or so was the radius of our vision) which, however, I could not help indulging in, while I rested. He made up his mind, and we were off again, straight and swift as an arrow this time, and in water deeper than the boathook. I could see by his face that he was taking some bold, expedient whose issue hung in the balance . . . Again we touched mud, and the artist's joy of achievement shone in his eyes. Backing away, we headed west, and for the first time he began to gaze into the fog.

'There's one!' he snapped at last. 'Easy all!'

A boom, one of the usual upright saplings, glided out of the mist. He caught hold of it and we brought up.

'Rest for three minutes now,' he said. 'We're in fairly good time.'

It was 11.10. I ate some biscuits and took a nip of whisky while Davies prepared for the next stage.

We had reached the eastern outlet of Memmert Balje, the channel which runs east and west behind Juist Island, direct to the south point of Memmert. How we had reached it was incomprehensible to me at the time, but the reader will understand by comparing my narrative with the dotted line on the chart. I add this brief explanation, that Davies's method had been to cross the channel called the Buse Tief, and strike the other side of it at a point well *south* of the outlet of the Memmert Balje (in view of the northward set of the ebb-tide), and then to drop back north and feel his way to the outlet. The check was caused by a deep indentation in the Itzendorf Flat; a *cul-de-sac*, with a wide mouth, which Davies was very near mistaking for the Balje itself. We had no time to skirt dents so deep as that; hence the dash across its mouth with the chance of missing the upper lip altogether, and of either being carried out to sea (for the slightest error was cumulative) or straying fruitlessly along the edge.

The next three miles were the most critical of all. They included the 'watershed', whose length and depth were doubtful; they included, too, the crux of the whole passage, a spot where the channel forks, our own branch continuing west, and another branch diverging from it north-westward. We must row against time, and yet we must negotiate that crux. Add to this that the current was against us till the watershed was crossed; that the tide was just at its most baffling stage, too low to allow us to risk short cuts, and too high to give definition to the banks of the channel; and that the compass was no aid whatever for the minor bends.

'Time's up,' said Davies, and on we went.

I was hugging the comfortable thought that we should now have booms on our starboard for the whole distance; on our starboard, I say, for experience had taught us that all channels running parallel with the coast and islands were uniformly boomed on the northern side. Anyone less confident than Davies would have succumbed to the temptation of slavishly relying on these marks, creeping from one to the other, and wasting precious time. But Davies knew our friend the 'boom' and his eccentricities too well; and preferred to trust to his sense of touch, which no fog in the world could impair. If we happened to sight one, well and good, we should know which side of the channel we were on. But even this contingent advantage he deliberately sacrificed after a short distance, for he crossed over to the *south* or unboomed side and steered and sounded along it, using the Itzendorf Flat as his handrail, so to speak. He was compelled to do this, he told me afterwards, in view of the crux, where the converging lines of booms would have involved us in irremediable confusion. Our branch was the southern one, and it followed that we must use the southern bank, and defer obtaining any help from booms until sure we were past that critical spot.

For an hour we were at the extreme strain, I of physical exertion, he of mental. I could not get into a steady swing, for little checks were constant. My right scull was for ever skidding on mud or weeds, and the backward suck of shoal water clogged our progress. Once we were both of us out in the slime tugging at the dinghy's sides: then in again, blundering on, I found the fog bemusing, lost all idea of time and space, and felt like a senseless marionette kicking and jerking to a mad music without tune or time. The misty form of Davies as he sat with his right arm swinging rhythmically forward and back, was a clockwork figure as mad as myself, but didactic and gibbering in his madness. Then the boathook he wielded with a circular sweep began to take grotesque shapes in my heated fancy: now it was the antenna of a groping insect, now the crank of a cripple's self-propelled perambulator, now the alpenstock of a lunatic mountaineer who sits in his chair and climbs and climbs to some phantom 'watershed'. At the back of such mind as was left me lodged two insistent thoughts: 'we must hurry on,' 'we are going wrong.' As to the latter, take a link-boy through a London fog and you will experience the same thing: he always goes the way you think is wrong. 'We're rowing *back*!' I remember shouting to Davies once, having become aware that it was now my left scull which splashed against obstructions. 'Rubbish,' said Davies, 'I've crossed over'; and I relapsed.

By degrees I returned to sanity, thanks to improving conditions. It is an ill wind that blows nobody good, and the state of the tide, though it threatened us with total failure, had the compensating advantage that the lower it fell the more constricted and defined became our channel; till the time came when the compass and boathook were alike unnecessary, because our handrail, the muddy brink of the channel, was visible to the eye, close to us; on our right hand always now, for the crux was far behind, and the northern side was now our guide. All that remained was to press on with might and main ere the bed of the creek dried.

What a race it was! Homeric, in effect: a struggle of men with gods, for what were the gods but forces of nature personified? If the God of the Falling Tide did not figure in the Olympian circle he is none the less a mighty divinity. Davies left his post, and rowed stroke. Under our united efforts the dinghy advanced in strenuous leaps, hurling miniature rollers on the bank beside us. My palms, seasoned as they were, were smarting with watery blisters. The pace was too hot for my strength and breath.

'I must have a rest,' I gasped.

'Well, I think we're over it,' said Davies.

We stopped the dinghy dead, and he stabbed over the side with the boathook. It passed gently astern of us, and even my bewildered brain took in the meaning of that.

'Three feet and the current with us. *Well* over it,' he said. 'I'll paddle on while you rest and feed.'

It was a few minutes past one and we still, as he calculated, had eight miles before us, allowing for bends.

'But it's a mere question of muscle,' he said.

I took his word for it, and munched at tongue and biscuits. As for muscle, we were both in hard condition. He was fresh, and what distress I felt was mainly due to spasmodic exertion culminating in that desperate spurt. As for the fog, it had more than once shown a faint tendency to lift, grown thinner and more luminous, in the manner of fogs, always to settle down again, heavy as a quilt.

Note the spot marked 'second rest' (approximately correct, Davies says) and the course of the channel, from that point westward. You will see it broadening and deepening to the dimensions of a great river, and finally merging in the estuary of the Ems. Note, too, that its northern boundary, the edge of the now uncovered Nordland Sand, leads, with one interruption (marked A), direct to Memmert, and is boomed throughout. You will then understand why Davies made so light of the rest of his problem. Compared with the feat he had performed, it was child's play, for he always had that visible margin to keep touch with if he chose, or to return to in case of doubt. As a matter of fact— observe our dotted line—he made two daring departures from it, the first purely to save time, the second partly to save time and partly to avoid the very awkward spot marked A, where a creek with booms and a little delta of its own interrupts the even bank. During the first of these departures, the shortest but most brilliant, he let me do the rowing, and devoted himself to the niceties of the course; during the second, and through the intermediate stages, he rowed himself, with occasional pauses to inspect the chart. We fell into a long, measured stroke, and covered the miles rapidly, scarcely exchanging a single word till, at the end of a long pull through vacancy, Davies said suddenly:

'Now, where are we to land?'

A sandbank was looming over us crowned by a lonely boom.

'Where are we?'

'A quarter of a mile from Memmert.'

'What time is it?'

'Nearly three.'

THE CRUISE OF THE *NONA*

Hilaire Belloc

They that go down to the sea in ships, that do business in great
    waters;
These see the works of the Lord, and his wonders in the deep.
For he commandeth, and raiseth the stormy wind, which lifteth
    up the waves thereof,
They mount up to the heaven, they go down again to the
    depths: their soul is melted because of trouble.
They reel to and fro, and stagger like a drunken man, and are at
    their wit's end.
Then they cry unto the Lord in their trouble, and he bringeth
    them out of their distresses.
He maketh the storm a calm, so that the waves thereof are still.
Then are they glad because they be quiet; so he bringeth them
    unto their desired heaven.

Psalm 107

Bardsey Sound

It was late in May, near midnight, the air being very warm and
still, and the sky not covered but somewhat dim, with no moon,
when I took the 'Nona' out from Holyhead harbour, having on
board one companion to help me work the boat, and a local man
who could speak Welsh for me in whatever places I might make
along the coast.

The very slight breeze, which had barely moved us through the
water after we had got up the anchor, died away long before we
reached the end of the breakwater, and it was necessary to pull her

31

out with the dinghy in order to fetch round the end of the
stonework and get to sea. There was at that time of the tide a little
current running towards the Stack, which would slightly help us
on our way once we were outside, and with this we drifted a full
hour and more, aided now and then by faint breaths of air, which
rose and died again like memories. So came we, with the turn of
the night, under the glare of the lighthouse at last, and then put
the nose of the little ship round for the point of Carnarvonshire and
the strait between the mainland and Bardsey Island, which is called
Bardsey Sound.

It was a course of about thirty-three miles, with no chance,
apparently, of covering it in all that night, nor perhaps in all the
coming day as well; for we had struck, as it seemed, that hot,
steady, summer weather in which one may play at a drifting match
for days on end.

While it was still dark the distant mountains could barely be
seen as something a little blacker than the sky. They looked
astonishingly low, as mountains always do on a moonless night,
when there is nothing to distinguish their details, and nothing
against which to compare them, or by which to tell their distance.
Already—it being now nearer two than one o'clock—a little wind,
had arisen, settling down, as it seemed, into somewhat east of
north, and blowing over the Anglesey flats. It gave us perhaps no
more than a couple of knots an hour, but it was heartening after
the long calm, and as we had all sail set she pulled to it steadily
enough. I was at the helm, my companion was still awake, sitting
in the cockpit and talking to me, and the hand who was to be with
us till we next landed smoked beside us on deck.

The wind had freshened somewhat, we were making perhaps
four or five knots, when the dawn began to show beyond Snowdon,
and those great hills at once looked higher against the glimmer of
grey light. Soon the whole coast was apparent, and Yr Eifl with its
triple peaks (clearer than I had expected; indeed, too clear for fine
weather) lay right ahead and Bardsey Island beyond it and the
narrow sound in between. The wind seemed steady, as though it

would hold. I reckoned that the tide would turn against us anywhere between six and seven in the morning, that it would turn back through the Sound about noon or one o'clock, and I calculated that we should be running into Cardigan Bay, past Bardsey, on the middle of the ebb, an hour or two later than that time.

But what happened was something wholly unexpected; it is always so at sea, and that is why it is said that the sea brings all adventures. Indeed, I think that as we go on piling measurements upon measurements, and making one instrument after another more and more perfect to extend our knowledge of material things, the sea will always continue to escape us. For there is a Living Spirit who rules the sea and many attendant spirits about him.

But on that brightening morning there was nothing to warn us. The glass was high and, if I remember right, still rising. The sky uncovered and clearer than it had been by night; the wind slight, but holding steady, and all was soldier's weather, so that any one could have taken that little ship through such weather where he would. It was weather, one would say, made for the instruction of the young in the art of sailing.

By the time it was fully light, we were making between six and seven knots, for the wind had sharply risen. As it was an off-shore wind, there was as yet no sea raised, but little tumbling white caps, very pleasant to look at, and all the movement coming on our quarter from over the land. With the rising of the sun it blew hard. We were yielding to it too much; we had taken down the topsail an hour before, and now I thought it wise to take in a reef as well, which we did in the headsail and the mainsail, but leaving the jib as it was, for that sail was not a large one.

I have sailed a great deal off and on in boats of this size (that is, somewhat more than thirty feet over all, with eight or nine feet beam, and drawing from five to six feet of water, cutter rigged), and I know it is an illusion; yet I can never get over the idea that a reef makes no difference. Two reefs—yes—but one reef I cannot 'feel'. It is an obtuseness in me; but so it is.

However, it seemed wiser to take in a reef of some sort, and two reefs would have reduced the sail quite unnecessarily, for it was not yet blowing so hard as all that.

We slipped down the coast smartly, nearing it all the time upon our slantwise course, and as we did so, the sun being now fully risen, it blew harder and harder every minute. A sea rose, a good following sea, but higher than one would have expected so nearly off the land from a land wind; and, as this boat has very little freeboard (it is her only defect, for she rises magnificently to the water, and bears herself better the worse the weather may be). I watched the swirl of the foam under her low counter as each wave slightly broke under the now fierce wind.

We shortened down to three reefs, but even so the helm was pulling hard, and when we changed jibs and put up the smallest we had, it griped more than I liked, straining my arm after so long a spell at the tiller. I handed it over to the man who was with us, and went forward to see that everything was clear, for it was now blowing really hard, and anything like a tangle if we got into difficulties would be dangerous. The gale rose . . . higher and the sea with it; but, tearing through the water as we now were under three reefs, we should soon make the Sound and get round the point of Carnarvonshire into easier water right under the lee of the land.

There was only one thing that troubled me, which was this question: should we make the Sound before the tide turned? It was an important question, because, although I had never been in those parts before, off-shore, in a boat of my own, yet I could judge that in such a piece of water, with all the Bay pouring through a channel barely two miles wide with a deep of barely one, the tide against such a gale would raise an impossible sea. If we could just make it on the tail of the tide, on the very last of the ebb, we should have nothing to bear but a strong following sea, such as that before which we were running at the moment: for the southerly stream was still strong under us. But if the water turned before we got into the Sound, we should have a time to remember; and so we did.

34

For I had done something or other to annoy the Earth Shaker, and he pursued me viciously, making the tide turn just before we reached the mouth of the Sound. In a time much shorter than I had expected, with no lull in between, the steady run of sea which had been combing behind us, towering above the counter, but regular and normal to deal with, turned into a confusion of huge tumbling pyramidal waves, leaping up, twisting, turning and boiling in such a confusion as I had never seen, not even in Alderney Race, which I had gone through many years before when I was a boy. The painter which held the dinghy to the stern parted, and that boat, a good and serviceable one, was lost. There was no question of turning in such a sea and under such a wind; the dinghy had to be abandoned. The tide against us was so fierce that even under that gale we hardly moved; and it was strange to see, from the leaping and struggling of the 'Nona', as the foam rushed by in a millrace, how steady remained the points on the Carnarvonshire shore, and how slowly we opened the Sound. The pace was irregular. There were moments when we advanced at perhaps a knot or a knot and a half against that fierce tide. There were others when we even slipped back. All the while the wind howled and the sea continued to rise and to boil in a cauldron more violent as the gale on the one hand and the tide against it on the other grew in strength, and in the fierceness of their struggle. In seas like this one never knows when some great tumbling lump of water may not break upon one's decks, for there is no run and follow, it is all confusion; and I remember thinking as I took the helm again in the midst of the turmoil of something I had seen written once of Portland Race: 'The sea jumps up and glares at you'—sound phrase.

We had thus (in some peril, but still able to keep a course, and, on the whole, advancing) got at last between the point and the Island, that is, to the heart of the Sound; and a very few yards would have brought us round out of the cauldron into smooth water and a run for some quiet anchorage right under the protection of the coast when (since at sea bad luck always goes gathering impetus) the jib blew out with a noise like a gun. A few rags hung on to its fastening; the rest of the canvas went away out to sea like a great wounded bird, and then sailed down and flopped into the seething of the water.

You may guess what that did to a boat in our straits! It made the helm almost impossible to hold with the violent gripe of the mainsail, half our head canvas being gone; and at the same time it stopped our way. We drifted back again into the worst of the water, and lost in five minutes what it had taken us more than an hour to make. The danger was real and serious. The man that was with us expressed his fears aloud; my companion, though new to the sea, took it all with great calm. As to what happened to myself, I will record it though it is a little detailed and personal: I will record it for the sake of the experience, of which others may make what they will.

I looked at the Carnarvonshire coast there close at hand, the sinking lines of the mountains as they fell into the sea, and I discovered myself to be for the first time in my life entirely indifferent to my fate. It was a very odd sensation indeed, like the sensation I fancy a man must have to find he is paralysed. Once, under the influence of a drug during an illness some such indifference had pervaded me, but here it was in the broad daylight and the sun well up above the mountains, with a clear sky, in the grip of a tremendous gale and of an angry countering sea, ravening like a pack of hounds. Yet I could only look with indifference on the sea and at the land. The sensation was about as much like courage as lying in a hammock is like a hundred yards race. It had no relation to courage, nor, oddly enough, had it any relation to religion, or to a right depreciation of this detestable little world which can be so beautiful when it likes.

Such as it was, there it was. I had always particularly disliked the idea of death by drowning, and I had never believed a word of the stories which say that at the end it is a pleasant death. Indeed, as a boy I was once caught under the steps of a swimming bath and held there a little too long before I could get myself out, and pleasant it was not at all. But here in Bardsey Sound, I was indifferent, even to death by drowning. All I was really interested in was to watch what way we lost and what chance we had of getting through.

Indeed, the whole question of fear is beyond analysis, and there is only one rule, which is that a man must try to be so much the master of himself that he shall be able to compel himself to do whatever is needful, fear or no fear. Whether there be merit or not in the absence of fear, which sentiment we call courage when it is allied to action, may be, and has been, discussed without conclusion since men were men. The absence of fear makes an admirable show, and excites our respect in any man; but it is not dependent upon the will. Here was I in very great peril indeed off Bardsey, and utterly careless whether the boat should, sink or swim; yet was I the same man who, in a little freshness of breeze that arose off the Owers a year or two ago, was as frightened as could well be—and with no cause. And if this be true of change of mood in one man, it must be true of the differences of mood in different men.

I had occasion during the war, when I had been sent to write upon the Italian front, to be swung to the high isolated rock of a mountain peak in the Dolomites by one of those dizzy wires which the Italian engineers slung over the gulfs of the Alps for the manning and provisioning of small high posts. It was an experience I shall ever remember, a vivid, hardly tolerable nightmare; but the man I was with, an Italian officer of great and deserved fame, earned during that campaign, not only felt nothing, but could not understand what my terror was. We sat, or rather lay, in one of those shallow trays which travel slowly along these wires over infinite deeps of air, and during the endless crawling through nothingness he told me, by way of recreation, the story of a private soldier who had been coming down from the isolated post some weeks before. The machinery had gone wrong, and the tray remained suspended over the gulf halfway across, for some twenty minutes. When it worked again and they hauled it in they found that the man had gone mad.

When the time came for the return journey, I very well

remember asking myself whether I had the control to face that second ordeal or no. It was an obscure crisis, unknown to others, but as real and as great within as any of those which stand out in fiction or history. I would rather have gone down by the path which clung to the steep, the precipitous mountain side. This was forbidden because it was under direct Austrian fire; I knew that I should not be allowed. So I faced the return—and it was worse than the going.

Also in my life I have known two men who have hunted lions, and each of them has told me that fear in the presence of peril from the beast was wholly capricious, and that sometimes when an exceedingly unpleasant death seemed certain, the man who had just missed his shot felt indifferent. I can be believe it.

Anyhow, here I was in Bardsey Sound, with many deaths moving over the howling fury of the sea, and not one of them affecting me so much as a shadow passing over a field.

The end of that adventure was odd and unreasonable—as things will be at sea. It was perhaps because we had been buffeted and pushed into some edge of the conflict between wind and water where the tide runs slacker; or it was perhaps because the wind had risen still higher. But, at any rate, after three separate raids forward (in the second of which we were very nearly out of our peril and into smooth water), and as many setbacks (one of which got us into the worst violence we had yet suffered), the 'Nona', in a fourth attempt (it was her own, not ours—we could do nothing but keep her, as best we might, to her course), slipped out and reached an eddy beyond the tide.

THREE MEN IN A BOAT

Jerome K. Jerome

He that would do good to another must do it in minute
particular. General good is the plea of the scoundrel,
hypocrite and flatterer.

Sailing

We pulled up in the backwater, just below Cookham, and had tea;
and, when we were through the lock, it was evening. A stiffish
breeze had sprung up—in our favour, for a wonder; for, as a rule
on the river, the wind is always dead against you whatever way you
go. It is against you in the morning, when you start for a day's
trip, and you pull a long distance, thinking how easy it will be to
come back with the sail. Then, after tea, the wind veers round, and
you have to pull hard in its teeth all the way home.

When you forget to take the sail at all, then the wind is
consistently in your favour both ways. But there! this world is only
a probation, and man was born to trouble as the sparks fly upward.

This evening, however, they had evidently made a mistake, and
had put the wind round at our back, instead, of in our face. We
kept very quiet about it, and got the sail up quickly before they
found it out, and then we spread ourselves about the boat in
thoughtful attitudes, and the sail bellied out, and strained, and
grumbled at the mast, and the boat flew.

I steered.

There is no more thrilling sensation I know of than sailing. It
comes as near to flying as man has got to yet—except in dreams.

The wings of the rushing wind seem to be bearing you onward, you know not where. You are no longer the slow, plodding, puny thing of clay, creeping tortuously upon the ground; you are a part of Nature! Your heart is throbbing against hers. Her glorious arms are round you, raising you up against her heart! Your Spirit is at one with hers; your limbs grow light! The voices of the air are singing to you. The earth seems far away and little; and the clouds so close above your head, are brothers, and you stretch your arms to them.

We had the river to ourselves, except that, far in the distance, we could see a fishing-punt, moored in midstream, on which three fishermen sat; and we skimmed over the water, and passed the wooded banks, and no one spoke.

I was steering.

As we drew nearer, we could see that the three men fishing seemed old and solemn-looking men. They sat on three chairs in the punt, and watched intently their lines. And the red sunset threw a mystic light upon the waters, and tinged with fire the towering woods, and made a golden glory of the piled-up clouds. It was an hour of deep enchantment, of ecstatic hope and longing. The little sail stood out against the purple sky, the gloaming lay around us, wrapping the world in rainbow shadows; and, behind us, crept the night.

We seemed like knights of some old legend, sailing across some mystic lake into the unknown realm of twilight, unto the great land of the sunset.

We did not go into the realm of twilight; we went slap into that punt, where those three old men were fishing. We did not know what had happened at first, because the sail shut out the view, but from the nature of the language, that rose up upon the evening air, we gathered that we had come into the neighbourhood of human beings, and that they were vexed and discontented.

Harris let the sail down, and then we saw what had happened. We had knocked those three old gentlemen off their chairs into a general heap at the bottom of the boat, and they were now slowly and painfully sorting themselves out from each other, and picking fish off themselves; and as they worked, they cursed us—not with a common cursory curse, but with long, carefully-thought-out, comprehensive curses, that embraced the whole of our career, and went away into the distant future, and included all our relations, and covered everything connected with us—good substantial curses.

Harris told them they ought to be grateful for a little excitement, sitting there fishing all day, and he also said that he was shocked and grieved to hear men their age give way to temper so.

But it did not do any good,

George said he would steer, after that. He said a mind like mine ought not to be expected to give itself away in steering boats— better let a mere commonplace human being see after that boat, before we jolly well all got drowned; and he took the lines, and brought us up to Marlow.

And at Marlow we left the boat by the bridge, and went and put up for the night at the 'Crown'.

41

ORDINARY FAMILIES

E. Arnot Robertson

There be three things which are too wonderful for me,
yea, four which I know not:

The way of an eagle in the air: the way of a serpent upon
a rock; the way of a ship in the midst of the sea; and the
way of a man with a maid.

Proverbs 30

The Treat

Basil and Stella Quest were joining us and the Cottrells for my
birthday treat which we had all been planning for weeks, a trip to
Littlehampton in two of our boats. Eleventh birthdays were considered
important in our family; a sort of half-way mark between nothing
and twenty-one: one chose the treat oneself. In their time Dru and
Ronald, both winter babies, had voted respectively for a pantomime
in London and an all-night punt-gunning expedition with Father.
That superlatively uncomfortable sport being at its best in the hardest
weather, Ronald's choice had been much admired by us all. Secretly
yearning for another pantomime I was sorry that my birthday fell
at the end of May, for this impelled me to do the Rush thing too
and ask for a sailing trip. It was the time of the year I most enjoyed
at Pin Mill because the bird tides had just set in, and I could go
nesting along the shore with Ted, Sootie Mawley's son and my great
friend; but Father's approval was everything, and so I had dutifully
worked myself into a state of excitement about my chosen treat.

*

44

Father busied himself in getting both boats in condition to start at a moment's notice, or as much in condition as our boats could be. They were used all the year round, for he was always buying and selling small craft, and as he could never spare the time or the money to give them a proper fit-out they were in a chronic state of overhaul. At the moment, *Wanderer*'s mizen mast was badly sprung and some child was constantly being shouted at not to lean against it or the shrouds; and the *Guadalupe*'s topmast backstays wanted replacing.

She was a new racing cruiser which made everyone less water-innocent than the Cottrells gasp at the huge spread of canvas carried on so slim a hull. Father had arranged that the Cottrell children were to travel aboard her, knowing that their mother (in the safe old *Wanderer*) would not be able to judge beforehand from *Guadalupe*'s lines what sort of performance this boat could put up in a sea. We had been warned to say nothing to the Cottrells of the terrifying liveliness of our latest acquisition. As a friend of the family Father was always eager to do the pampered Cottrell children good against their parents' will.

I was in *Wanderer*. Her sails flapped, and filling the intervals between the grunts of the boom, as it swung over lazily, the reef points kept up a quick, light pattering on the canvas. Most sailing people loathe that sound, connecting it in memory with hours of helpless rolling, becalmed in Channel or North Sea swells; but we made a point of liking it, being proud of our hard-won detachment from our stomachs. 'Lord, yes,' Father would say to anyone who inquired about any of our worse passages, 'all my troupe were sick as dogs. Doesn't affect them, though. Get used to it, you know. They carry on all right.' And we glowed. Dru positively gloried in cutting to the minimum the necessary pause in her work. As the eldest of us she had had even more experience, and a well-timed turn of her head was all that was now required. I envied her; this was so awfully Rush. I think she enjoyed seasickness as a means of earning Father's commendation.

It just crossed my mind to be thankful that here, six miles up the river, we had no swell to contend with, only scorching sun reflected back into our eyes from the smooth, heavy-looking water. Except by going below, where it was unbearably stuffy, there was no way of keeping in the shade while the slack sails shifted continually. It is practically always unpleasantly hot in a small boat, on the very rare occasions when it is not uncomfortably cold in the wind from which, like the sun, there is no chance of shelter on deck. Shocked by my own thoughts, I wrenched my mind away from this disloyal reflection on our beloved hobby.

'Oh, Mum*mee*! You haven't put in my blue dress! And I'm too *hot* in this one. I *told* you . . .' Marnie's voice carried across from the *Guadalupe*.

'. . . But Eleanor, butter is *always* kept in that tin, dipped in sea water occasionally to cool it . . .'

'It won't, dear . . . Air and water the same temperature . . . may feel cooler . . . go rancid just as easily . . . bacterial action . . . water . . .'

'. . . Not *sea* water, Eleanor . . . Always *has* been kept in that tin . . .' Like Father and Mr Cottrell, Mother and Mrs Cottrell were inclined to talk down to each other, whenever they disagreed on some point like this, on which each had some reason to feel superior. The Cottrells were scientifically well-informed, as well as artistic, but then Mother was a Rush, and as such surely entitled to speak with authority of the benign qualities of the local ocean.

'. . . So I happened to be in that part of Chile when he brought off the raid—Gosh, what a chap he was!' (in his modest recitals Father always 'happened' to be in just those places where the revolution, earthquake, epidemic, or other interruption of humdrum life also 'happened' to take place at the same time. It was not until you knew him well that you realised that if Arthur Rush were anywhere within reach of the locality, there was about as much chance in this coincidence as in the 'happening' together of iron and magnet.) 'And the trouble from the first with the punitive expedition we organised—What, Basil? Well, yes, as a matter of fact I was. There didn't happen to be anyone else to take command.

The trouble was that it wasn't clear which side was getting the punishment.—My men got sunstroke in the plains and frostbite as soon as we got into the mountains, and day after day we never saw the fellows we were after, but they got away with some of our equipment every few hours.—Margaret! let go of that mizen stay: how many more times—?' The Quest children had never heard the bandit story, though they had asked for it often enough, and I could not hear it too often. They were lucky today: one could not generally prise it out of Father so soon after a re-telling.

Still, when it was over, time stretched out again rather boringly just when it was not wanted. Excellent time, minutes that I should soon wish, in vain, to slip into some other situation to prolong it, now crawled by unfilled, and I could not do anything about it. Consolingly, three shelduck alighted on the water between us and the shore, planing down over our heads at the extraordinary landing-speed of these birds. Simultaneously, as they whistled by in line, the scarlet legs withdrew from the belly-feathers that had covered all but the curled toes, and stuck out stiffly in front of the hurtling bodies. The birds might have been drilling by numbers, so exactly together were their movements: it always seemed to be a matter of pride with them in this, the mating season, to slacken speed as little as they dared until the last second. Fascinated, I used to watch these showy creatures by the hour as they took off or landed on the water. Now, at the same instant, all the brilliant webbed toes turned upwards and opened widely, to go skithering over the water as the birds braked suddenly, with vertical winds. Even so, the impact of the tough little bodies sent up, as one, three small fountains of spray. Two drakes were courting a female. They settled down close to the *Guadalupe*, wagging their tails and muttering discontentedly as though the rivals were criticising one another's performance in taking the water. Having had the biological wisdom to develop a flavour like stewed sawdust, which no method of cooking can disguise, this handsome black, white, and orange bird increases yearly on the east coast, where the dull but edible teal and widgeon are dwindling in numbers.

Those three shelduck, with the heron that has drifted delicately from one clump of trees to another on the edge of the marsh the year before, still fly through my memory of those days, with the troubling graciousness of a child's sense of some new quality in familiar things—still cut, in a grey and in a cloudless sky, wider than any skies seem nowadays, the lovely lines along which I hold them transfixed in movement—still may be recalled in clearer detail than the people or the circumstances in which, at the time, I was really engrossed.

They swam away with a curved arrowhead of ripple spreading out further and further from each breast across the still water, while on the other side of us the surface of the river darkened all at once, and crumpled before a puff of wind from the south-east. The boom swung over again, less lazily, and the reef points stopped tapping.

'Going to hold! Get under way, Ronald,' shouted Father to the other boat and went below to start up our auxiliary engine, in order to keep pace with the faster *Guadalupe* under sail alone.

The venerable marine motor, which only Father could coax into action, gave what sounded like a series of apologetic coughs and expired with another hiccough. Afterwards it would only hiccough. Then it refused to do that. Father put his head out of the hatch to say, 'Battery's shorted. Damn!' his eyes shining with pleasure. He settled down to the most congenial occupation possible for him as professional engineer on holiday, tinkering with an engine that he was not paid to run. 'Cast off, someone. Lallie, it's your trip, you steer.'

The light breeze hardened. We tacked in the wake of the *Guadalupe*. Instantly time began to tear along, much too fast, because I had just discovered, with a burning curiosity to know why, that there was something delightful about those curving arrowheads of ripple, which the wind was rapidly confusing with many others, of uninteresting shape. They mattered in the same incomprehensible way in which a heron's flight had lately begun to

48

matter, and something about Margaret had always mattered, or for as long as I could remember.

I looked at her: she, too, was glancing back, watching the swimming shelduck creasing the water with little forward surges of their puffy breasts, but what she thought about anything I could rarely guess or ask. With a child's anxiety to get everything clear and settled I wondered whether the spreading ripples could have been quite so . . . whatever they were, exciting or touching, but anyway important—if they had not been shaped to those curves but had been only triangular ridges in the water.

'Move, Lallie! I can't get at the sheet. Whatever are you looking at, dear?' Mother asked as I craned my neck round desperately for a second while *Wanderer* gathered way, trying to see the last of the ripples before the wind obliterated them. For the moment I had forgotten the dangerous presence of older people. Returning my attention to the course, I felt myself turning scarlet, because I had been surprised doing something much more seriously private than the things that no one was supposed to see you doing. I was deciding hurriedly that it would probably have mattered just about as much, but in a different way. Time, gathering itself indolently all the morning, had now leapt forward and grabbed the only thing I wanted at the moment.

'Nothing,' I said, turning to give one more glance astern; but trying, too late, to give the glance a casual appearance. It was annoying to have to decide, at random, and in a hurry like this, a problem which I felt was really important.

'Now, Lallie, what is it?' said Mother, smiling and Olympian, and positively hateful for the moment.

I knew that the treacherous crimson was spreading round my ears. Oh, Hoogie, *Hoogie* don't let anyone find out, and laugh! One must not pray to the Holy Virgin against Mother, but Hoogie would not matter, and Hoogie would understand.

'What a long way ahead *Guadalupe* is getting!' said Mrs Gottrell with sudden forced brightness. Intuitively she was trying to trail a red herring for me, I knew, because my face had already given me away. 'Why is she faster than this boat when this boat is so much bigger, Phyllis?'

Evidence of her care never to force the confidence of a child always had the effect of making my thoughts feel miserably naked before her imagination. Echoes from other occasions when Mrs Cottrell had tiptoed away from the holy ground of my immature mind still rang loudly in my memory. If possible, I grew hotter, resenting her intrusive sympathy more than Mother's curiosity.

'Racier build—larger sail area for her size, Eleanor. Come on, Lallie, out with the big secret!'

Why did grown women make such a kindly fuss when one came in with a skinned knuckle, and then do this sort of thing lightly at other times? What made them resent instinctively the mystery and excitement of this vague something in the mind—the something that the ripple of a flying heron called into being? They tried to prevent one from discovering about it by laughing, or being too understanding, or asking one to run an errand for them and not waste time, whenever one was getting tinglingly close to it. In their dull kingdom of food and talk they felt shut out of it, and women more than men did not like to feel that about anything, I knew already. Women were afraid of this unknown spirit, which called through quite ordinary voices, like curlews' over the water at night: it was the thing that took men such as Father away from them into wild corners of the world, and could take even children like me out of their reach for a while, though they could bring us back and hurt us for going. Perhaps they half knew that one day they would not be able to recall us at will.

'Oh, well then to balance that, I suppose she draws more water than we do?' (Mrs Cottrell surreptitiously squeezed my shoulder to show me that I had an ally.)

'Yes, Eleanor; you're getting quite intelligent about sailing!— you know, this queer kid gets the oddest notions in her head—' (Mrs Cottrell frowned reprovingly at Mother for me. Curse her, oh curse her! But Mother did not notice.) 'What on earth has she got hold of now? Be a sport and tell a pal, Lallie!'

I thought that in a moment I should have to be rude; often one's only resource in childhood. It would cause a rotten sort of distraction, but at least they would not then get at the ripples, which Mrs Cottrell had now turned into something about which I was somehow ashamed, instead of just something that I wanted to keep to myself.

'Birds,' said Margaret, turning her indifferent glance from the far-off duck to me, and my heart stood still with fear. 'Lallie doesn't want people to know she's mad about them. She'd like to cry now because those three ducks came down on the water when we were on the mooring and she can't watch them. Thinks they're wonderful. Just shelduck! And herons. Thinks they're all hers!'

Margaret laughed, and Mother, too, of course, and asked more questions, and Mrs Cottrell deliberately asked none, and my whole secret world crashed about me, along with the ruins of that day's hoped-for enjoyment. They made me sound a fool in the hearing of Father, whom I loved better than anyone else, and because I was eleven years old that was almost intolerable, but after a time, between them all, they somehow made the birds seem silly, too, and that was much worse.

It is hard to guess what sense reveals to people like Margaret things far beyond the compass of their understanding. I had never told her anything that went on in my mind, because she never told me anything. This was the first occasion, as far as I remember, on which she spoilt for me something that I greatly valued, not from malice, but through her own indifference to such things. She was superbly armoured against revenge, caring for no one and nothing herself.

Robust humour was a speciality in our family, and being laughed at was considered a tonic automatically wholesome for anyone at any time, with the exception of God, who alone was not supposed to be improved by having His corners rubbed off (Mother's favourite expression) with this strong mental abrasive: the Old Testament contained too many records of His inability to take a joke in good part; but save on sacred subjects one was always safe in being funny with a Rush; it was part of the home-made tradition.

'Look, Lallie, there's a kittiwake gull—are you going all goosey over it? Why don't you write it a little poem?'

And because the day was done for anyway, so that now it wasn't worth while being rude and standing all the fuss that would follow, I grinned and played up to them as the quickest way of getting this wretchedness over.

'It *is* a kittiwake, isn't it?—Of course, you know them all on the wing, don't you?'

Angrily I grinned harder and told them I only knew the ordinary birds, and anyway it was a blackcap, not a kittiwake. Out of the wreck of my joy in birds, which could never be quite the same again now that people knew of it, I saved just this one species, saved it even from Mrs Cottrell. They could go on being funny or sympathetic if they liked about the kittiwake; I had crept into a small unhappy security inside my own mind, from which I would with less effort smile out on their ignorance that it was a white tern, one of the exquisite little diving birds which fishermen call sea-swallows. But now they could not get at it and make it look as stupid as they could me, for the bird they spoilt with their nonsense did not exist. As if any kittiwake ever bounced off the water in that entrancing way when it dived!

'Well, I'm afraid I'm not much interested in birds,' said Mrs Cottrell with dogged protectiveness. 'I must say, Phyllis, *Guadalupe* looks a much more dangerous support for my entire offspring now that she's going along leaning over on her side'—very properly Mother shot her a horrified look at this description of our finest boat listing in a good breeze—'than she did at anchor. I suppose she is quite sound, isn't she?'

'"Anchor"—Oh, my God!' Father from below suddenly leapt up into the cockpit. 'Does Ronald know that the new cable's in two parts?—I forgot to shackle it. There's only about six fathoms of loose chain on *Guadalupe*'s anchor. My best, too! The stockless one, Phyl! Does Sootie know? Pull yourselves together, people, and think!'

None of us, of course, had any idea. Father bounded forward and hallooed from the bows after the other boat, but *Guadalupe* was now about half a mile ahead, dead to windward. No one on board could hear. Seeing him shouting, they hallooed back cheerily. The breeze had been hardening all the time; we were both cutting through a jabble of rising sea at a fair speed, but they were much faster than we were without the engine. Mrs Cottrell, the adoring mother, was probably the only person in Pin Mill who did not know that all the fishermen, uncertain of the pronunciation of the new boat's real name, called her the Gawdelpus because she was much too lean and tender to stand safely the length of mast and sail area which Father had given her.

'Arthur, what will happen?—I don't quite understand—I mean, it doesn't matter, does it?' Mrs Cottrell was alarmed—' I mean, the children . . .'

'Eleanor, don't be an ass,' said Father in the heat of the moment, dancing grotesquely on deck to attract the attention of the other boat. 'Does it matter? When they bring up they'll chuck the thing over and just stand watching the damn' chain run out, and then tinkle-tinkle, splash-splash, good-bye my anchor! And six fathoms of chain.'

'Yes, but it won't—They'll be all right, won't they? If the boat—er—drags in this wind . . .?'

'It won't "drag," ' said Father impatiently, continuing to dance about. 'There won't be an anchor to drag! No kedge on board. They'll probably run her aground in the flap, though. But anyway, it's not the children who'll go overboard. Only the anchor, damn it. Children float.'

Ronald, very pleased with himself for being left in charge of a party with Sootie, got up on deck and danced back, and Marnie, Lester, and Dru performed gnomelike actions in support. They held on. Passing ahead of us, a puff of wind with extra weight in it laid *Guadalupe* over till the lee rail was awash: it took nothing of a breeze to do that. She drew still further away from us.

'Blast! We'll have to chase them. Phyl, get out the topsail.'

'Arthur, you can't chase Gawdelpus in this boat!' Mother protested. Catching the nickname that we had kept from her, Mrs Cottrell asked several questions which no one had time to answer smoothly.

The sail went up in record time. With our increased speed we just held them, but Ronald, thinking that Father was making a sporting effort to race him, replied with his big reaching foresail as *Guadalupe* rounded an elbow in the river and the wind came freer. She drew away again; but the wind was gathering weight every minute. It was now stiff enough to be perfect for us and a little too much for the lighter craft. If it hardened any more we might catch her yet, for with that absurd length of mast she would have to heave-to and reef. We chased her hopefully past Bloody Point, through Harwich harbour, and out to the Naze and the open sea, where the wind blowing against the tide was already kicking up short steep waves.

Everyone badly needed a meal by now, but all the cooked food that had not been condemned as surplus by Father had been stowed on board *Guadalupe*, and with *Wanderer* as lively as she was at the moment it was asking too much of anyone's stomach to expect Primus cookery down below. Father, to whom food never meant much, was not going to sacrifice his anchor to a meal by heaving-to for a while. Once out of the harbour he took the tiller and gave a marvellous display of boat handling, cutting in over the tricky underwater sandbanks that lay shorewards in a way that Ronald and even Sootie dared not do, saving yards here and cheating a current there, taking advantage of every favourable shoot of tide, keeping me or Margaret sounding all the time, and getting the ponderous long-keeled *Wanderer* round on the other tack with almost the ardour of a racing boat whenever either of us sang out that the bottom was shelving up again to within a foot or so of our keel.

'I really think you'd better give up the anchor, dear,' said Mother, who was nearly always right and after sixteen years with Father had not yet learnt to refrain from advising him at such times. She was envisaging the boat piled up and holed on the chalk-humps with which the sands hereabouts are strewn.

We were level with *Guadalupe* but about a mile inshore of her when Ronald, furious at being overhauled by the old *Wanderer*, ran up his flying jib in spite of knowing the dubious condition of the topmast backstays—and undoubtedly in spite of Sootie's protests. Now *Guadalupe*'s hull was only visible at intervals because of the pother she made, driven like that through steep water, and she took the lead again. The seas were not yet vicious, but we were all drenched through on board the stout *Wanderer*: it was easy to see that Mrs Cottrell, growing greener and greener and trying not to gasp when sheets of spray came over, was imagining without difficulty exactly what her children must be suffering in a boat shipping solid water at every plunge.

We held on, using all our resources for speed, but catching up with *Guadalupe* was now no longer Father's prime concern. We must be at hand in case of an accident. His silence about Ronald's extraordinary foolhardiness was more eloquent than anything the rest of us said of the grave risk to their masthead. A broken mast, which Ronald was courting, was a really expensive item.

'Arthur, I know I'm being ridiculously maternal,' said Mrs Cottrell apologetically, 'but it is dangerous, isn't it, when a boat gets dismasted?'

'Oh, only with bad luck,' said Father, who could never take seriously the Cottrells' fear of the water. 'One of the big racers lost a hand that way this year, and a French boat—one of the 12 metre—she lost two. But quite often a falling mast doesn't kill anybody. Believe me, I'm with you at the moment in your hope that if either of our sons cops it, it'll be mine, not yours.'

'Arthur, I really don't think . . .' Mother began, and then, in her quietest tone, 'Oh, look, what a pity!'

Through the smother of spray round *Guadalupe* we saw a billow of flapping canvas, and the top of the mainsail sagging over into a tangle of broken gear

'*What* a pity,' said Mother again gently. 'How silly of Ronald.'

Even after this we could not get near enough to shout a warning to them about the anchor. *Guadalupe*'s mainsail, being a Bermudan, would not come down with the top of the mast broken, and holding almost as much wind as before, continued to drive her faster than *Wanderer*, with Sootie and Ronald doing their best to lash up the hanging masthead and the flapping head of the sail. Clearly they were making for the shelter of the Colne off Brightlingsea. The position at last warranted Mrs Cottrell's anxiety, for the wind now came in strong squalls and *Guadalupe* was burdened with a heavy press of canvas that could not be lightened. *Wanderer*, too, ought to have shortened sail, but Father still held on in case of further trouble aboard the other boat.

Cold, frightfully hungry, and feeling increasingly queasy in consequence, we chased them all the way—a four-hour passage— and watched their mainsail split right across, as Father expected, in the troublesome patch of water which seethes round the Bar buoy in the Colne estuary.

Instead of sailing on into the harbour, they brought up, again exactly as Father feared, as soon as they were under the shelter of East Mersea shore. Had they gone on into Brightlingsea there was a chance of their picking up a mooring, and so saving the anchor for which we had worked so hard. But when we were still about a quarter of a mile behind them they rounded up nicely into the wind and, in spite of our despairing howls, threw the anchor over and idly stood by watching the first few fathoms of cable run out through the fairlead. At the sight of the loose end of the chain, Dru flung herself gallantly down on it, and was dragged half over the bow, losing bits of skin on the way. Ronald gripped her legs and they hung on grimly, and then, as the remnants of the mainsail could not be brought down in a hurry, though Sootie made a heroic attempt, the torn canvas filled with wind, the *Guadalupe* bowed her broken mast towards us ironically and began to sail herself. The chain was dragged out of their hands, to disappear under water. We anchored at once. They got the boat under control as quickly as the ill-balanced canvas allowed, missed going ashore by what must have been inches, and sailed back towards us. Having seen the figure of her son leaning negligently against the mast through-out the anchoring flap, while Marnie sat in the well and waved to us with equal calm, the relieved Mrs Cottrell went down and was sick, before grappling splendidly with the Primus stoves to get us all some food.

We on deck made ready to hand over to *Guadalupe* our spare anchor and warp. To do this we needed their dinghy; ours had been left behind to save its drag on *Wanderer*'s speed. *Guadalupe* manoeu-vred to slide by *Wanderer*'s stern so that the dinghy towrope could be passed to us.

'Way enough! Way enough, you fools? shouted Father as they tacked up to us, in spite of knowing that one should never interfere with the management of another boat. But the loss of the anchor had disturbed Father's confidence in both Ronald and Sootie, and they seemed to be shooting up to us too hard. The dejected Ronald at the tiller looked startled by the command, and Sootie, in the bow, even more so: the boat turned further into the wind, losing all steerage way abreast of us. Then, suddenly, *Guadalupe*'s foresail filled, bringing her bow swinging towards us. Nothing that Ronald could do now would turn her back; the tattered mainsail was no match for the foresail, and she bore down relentlessly upon *Wan-derer*.—'Enough, E N O U G H!' shouted Father again, futilely, as Sootie made frantic efforts to let go the foresail halyard. *Guadalupe*'s bowsprit came across us between our shrouds and mast. There was a rending noise as our chainplates on that side buckled and tore out, and a horrible cracking of the rail of one or both boats as they ground together, fairly ravening for each other's tender topsides.

'What-the hell-think you were doing-Sootie?' Father gasped between enormous exertion to part the boats.

'What-you-say-'luff'-for, sir?' Sootie gasped reproachfully.

'"Enough" not "luff"—you fool!'

57

'Yessir.'

'You-didn't!' panted Ronald.

'I wondered what you said "luff" for, Daddy,' Margaret remarked dreamily as she stood beside him, taking no part in the mix-up.

'Oh, my God!' said Father with an air of wild resignation, letting up the strain he was keeping on the encroaching bowsprit. 'If everyone's gone mad in this boat as well . . .!' He lit a cigarette and sauntered below to help Mrs Cottrell, a little comforted, no doubt, by the knowledge that no other sailing man in the world could leave the scene of a marine accident like that. The rest of us spent many hours clearing up the wreckage.

'Clean, wholesome fare,' remarked Lester Cottrell, apropos of nothing, half-way through the meal which followed. The *Wanderer*, where we had all gathered to eat because *Guadalupe* was dancing around her anchor in the swell, rolled ponderously from side to side, occasionally throwing in a slight pitch. He gazed distastefully at the marvels of food which his mother had produced. 'Excuse me a moment, Mrs Rush.' (Lester's manners were always faultless.) He disappeared on deck. Stella Quest was ill in sympathy shortly afterwards, but refused to turn in to her bunk as Mother suggested, because of her self-imposed task of helping to look after 'the little ones', as she maddeningly called Margaret and me. All the older people were very hearty, however, during the meal, and throughout the two days we were forced to spend in Brightlingsea, patching up the boats. We dredged at intervals with a grapnel for the anchor and chain, but failed to recover them; and they said it was all great fun, so I obediently supposed it was. Only Lester and Marnie were immune from that kind of suggestion: assured almost sharply by Mother that any child must enjoy a lovely exciting sail, Lester said plaintively, 'Yes, but Marnie and I aren't really adapted to childhood,' which earned him another peculiar look from Father.

Father inevitably became very matey indeed with the carpenter who came on board to re-build *Guadalupe*'s rail. Looking back, it occurs to me that Father must have had an exceptionally strong social sense to get the kick that he obviously did out of friendship with men of a different class.

An interesting little fellow (almost any dull-looking person became miraculously interesting when Father drew him out with self-effacing skill), the carpenter had been in Greenland during one of the great fish famines, when three open boats, manned by crews weakened by want of food, forced their way through the seventy miles of ice and wintry seas from Durhapp to Uigilak to bring relief. Father volunteered nothing of his own experiences in Greenland, merely asking a few knowledgeable questions: he was usually too modest to offer his personal account of any incident to which others referred. But somehow a pause occurred in the conversation into which the carpenter dropped the remark, 'You did ought to go there. A grand country, in a way,' much as though the words were being drawn from him by some spiritual magnet.

'Oh, I've been.' Carelessly. Just that; no more.

'Have you now! When was you there?'

'Same year as you. Look here, Harry, what's your boss going to charge me for this rail? I'm pretty broke, you know, through this smash-up. New cloths in the mainsail, mast shortened, new shrouds and chain plates, new anchor. Filthy luck, wasn't it?'

'*Where* was you?—Goo' lord, why . . .'

'Oh, there was a lot of bunk talked about the relief boats. We didn't have anything like such a time as people made out.—Tell him if the bill's small enough I may pay it: if not, I'll go bankrupt and he won't get a penny, there's a good chap.' And that was all. He firmly held the conversation off Greenland after this. So like Father. I thrilled with horror and anger when Ronald, sore after the slating he had earned over the dismasting, referred to him a little later as 'our self-conscious buccaneer'. I think Ronald himself was shocked as soon as he had said it. Basil Quest seemed unable to believe his ears. He had developed a boundless admiration for Father because of the Greenland business, a full-blooded, embarrassing hero-worship which lasted for years and was of a very different quality from Lester Cottrell's intellectual fancy for him. Lester approved of Ronald's description, and if the three boys had been more of an age—Basil was only eleven while the others were thirteen—his slow wits would probably have prompted threats of violence. My treat was going badly enough without that.

The outward journey, which was to have taken two days, lasted nearly a week. We finished all the ready cooked provisions, and the whole supply of butter went rancid, though it had always kept nicely in its perforated tin until Mrs Cottrell suggested that the laws of science were against it. Suppressed irritation started between us and the Cottrells; they felt that we ought to have learnt now to preserve butter on board, while we darkly suspected Marnie, who had been told off to dip it, of having taken the scientific view and scamped the job as useless—which, of course, it probably was. Still butter always had kept . . .

The trouble nearly came to a head over the saucepan which Mrs Cottrell condemned as dirty just when Mother was about to use it. As cook's assistant for the day, on whom the washing-up devolved, I privately thought it was quite clean enough for boat purposes: the Cottrells were fussy about that sort of thing. Mother thought as I did, but obligingly picked off a tiny piece of dried stuff sticking to the bottom.

'Only a bit of cauliflower, Eleanor.' (Greenstuff, we knew, was considered particularly wholesome by enlightened people like the Cottrells.)

'Only! My dear Phyllis, haven't you ever seen decaying vegetable matter under a microscope? Well, if you had . . .!'

There was a surface-friendly battle over the saucepan, in which Mother was too kind to use the strongest argument on her side, 'Well, we always cook like this and my children are healthier, not to say better-looking than yours!' Mrs Cottrell amiably called her by several rude names that we could not have used, and firmly took over all the cooking for the rest of the trip. It was hardly necessary for her to point out again that she was not one of those women who so annoyed her by marrying unexpected poverty and then

60

failing to become reconciled to it: we were, however, reminded by inference on several occasions during the next few days of her excellence in this respect. It was not until some years later, when I accidentally discovered that Mrs Cottrell had never been anything but desperately hard up and domesticated, that I really began to like this formerly too flawless woman.

I was sadly conscious that in Pin Mill the bird tides were practically wasting themselves without me. These two days of delay, when we could do nothing but wait about for ship-wrights and sail-makers, were infuriating. In the seabirds' breeding season—May to July, later than on land—the tides slacken all round this coast, by what seems like a pure dispensation of a bird-minded Providence, so that the terns, shelducks and many of the gulls can safely raise their beach-coloured families among the litter flung up by the full spring tides. Ted, bother him, must be stealing any number of marches on me by locating the first eggs. My one consolation was that Father, tinkering the recalcitrant engine, became lavish with the loveliest stories. I heard for the first time of his idiotic escapade as a young man in Chile, when he was trying to find his way across the Anje mountains on the sort of horse that stops if one holds its head up, and stumbles if one lets it down. He knew only vaguely the whereabouts of the nitrate prospector with whom he meant to join up for a while. (I decided on my own that he was probably going to the man's assistance, but he did not tell us that: Father was much freer with accounts of being made ridiculous than with stories in which he could not help figuring as life size, or over. But there were so many of both kinds in his strange store of memories that new ones were always coming to the surface, 'like bubbles in a stagnant pond' as the Quests' extraordinary father once remarked, prompted no doubt by jealousy.) Having swum a ford in a flooded mountain torrent, where he lost the horse because it turned back carrying his clothes and supplies on its back, he arrived half-naked at a dilapidated shanty. Here he took over the effects of a British surveyor who had died some years before. The only wearing apparel not hopelessly damaged by ants was a

complete Charterhouse soccer kit, lovingly kept in a zinc trunk—
the sort of expected unexpectedness of the wilds. Feeling that in
this part of the world the solecism should pass uncondemnned.
Father pressed on in this striking get-up, and reached the man he
had come to join after an appalling march in which fever from the
immersion was only one of his troubles. It'll be just my luck, he
thought, if the fellow turns out to be an Old Carthusian, and
resents the rig. Swaying as he stood, on the verge of collapse, he
went through an emotional parody of the Dr Livingstone-I-presume
meeting of white men in isolated places.

'Good God! Rush!' said a cockney voice which relieved him of
the Charterhouse apprehension. 'You were at Wanstead Grammar
School with me!'

'Yes,' said Father, while the ground heaved and receded before
his eyes. He had some vague memory of helping to scrag this scion
of a socialist family for airing his father's views. 'As a matter of
fact . . .'

'Then why that bloody shirt? Eton, or Harrow is it?'

'Charterhouse, I believe,' said Father. 'But as . . .'

'Good God! Isn't the old school good enough for you?'

'Yes,' said Father, 'and as a matter of fact . . .'

'That's rich, that is! Thought you'd get away with the haw-haw
stuff here, did you? . . . Think I'd demean myself wearing a class
badge . . . ticks like you who let down the workers . . . bolstering
up the capitalist system . . .' and a good deal more Father heard
just before he became unconscious, and when he came round again
he found himself alone with a small—a very small—store of food.
So after a short rest he walked back across the mountains, and
crawled weakly to an outpost of civilisation in semi-nakedness, for
safety's sake, having left the offending shirt on the other side of the
ford, which he had re-swum.

Oh, a marvellous man; I could not imagine what Mr Quest
could have meant when he accepted Father's invitation to his
children for the treat—'Delighted, Rush, I'm regrettably devoid of
the glamour o' far places myself. Pump it into them. Pump it into

them. Such a normalising influence.' There had been something funny about his tone. There always was. Surely a dank sort of person like Mr Quest ('dank' was Lester's word for him) who did not care much about his own children must admire Father and enjoy hearing his experiences?

Mrs Cottrell had another of her delicate moments when we reached Littlehampton at last and she prepared to go ashore to shop. Picking up what she imagined to be Mother's shopping list, she took off the table a piece of paper which Marnie had just laid down. Marnie protested crossly that it was her drawing. Without thinking, Mrs Cottrell glanced at the scrawl and then apologised charmingly for looking at an unfinished sketch without permission. The older Cottrells had the modern parents' conscientiousness in disclaiming rights of discourtesy over their children. Recalling them now, I fancy their disclaimers sounded very much like high-principled wallowings in the joy of self-abasement: at the moment I was stunned with envy of Marnie.

'I was drawing the back of a wave, and you've wah wah wah.' When Marnie was in a bad temper her adenoids became obstructive.

'Darling, I'm sorry. I didn't really look at it. I think I had it upside down.'

'It wasn't nearly done. And now you've gone and spoilt it all.'

'Oh, Marnie, I haven't, have I? I know just how you feel. I loathe people looking at my rough designs. I wouldn't have looked at it without asking you if I'd thought. Honestly I didn't mean to.'

'. . . you've *crumpled* it!' wailed Marnie, who was really longing, I knew of old, for someone to take an interest in her extraordinary drawing. She would thoroughly have enjoyed being the centre of the sort of attention that I had endured over the shelducks, but in this her adoring parents always thwarted her with kindliness and tact. Like a psychological angel, Mrs Cottrell persisted in not treading where the inrush of fools would have been welcome. She asked diffidently, while helping Marnie to straighten out imaginary creases, to be allowed to see the drawing when it was quite, quite finished, and Marnie nodded sulkily, knowing that it never would be. How could anyone be expected to finish the drawing of a back of a wave when none of the beastly things would keep still enough to be properly studied?

At Littlehampton, as usual in seaside places, there was nothing to do. Perspiring women, tightly encased in black, towed shrilly protesting children along the shadeless promenade showering them with threats in whose execution the experienced children obviously disbelieved. Over the sands as well, and for several yards out into the sea, brooded that atmosphere of vague maternal menace which is peculiar to English coastal resorts. For want of occupation all the children of the party fell under the spell of a Salvation Army band. We returned to the boats singing 'I'm so H-A-P-P-Y' (*fortissimo*) 'for I'm S-A-V-E-D!' (smug *pianissimo*) to the distress of both the mothers on board. It would be hard to say which of them disliked the hymn more, Mother for religious reasons, or Mrs Cottrell because of the deep Cottrell prejudice against everything of that kind. On the whole we took our religion more lightly than they took their agnosticism. Even the superior Lester could not be weaned from this catchy tune, and such was the religious feeling it engendered that Ronald and Lester were moved to sneak ashore on our last afternoon and cadge a Bible off the delighted leader of the band, in order to study those parts of the Old Testament which had not been thought suitable reading matter for the children of either family. They had always meant to see what was in the Book of Judges to make my mother take the Mawleys' Bible hurriedly out of Marnie's hands one day, when we were all having tea at Sootie's cottage and Marnie, as usual, settled down to read the nearest thing to hand. After surreptitious skimmings of the 19th and 20th chapters on the way home, both came to the same conclusion. Ronald said proudly that the bits not dull were bawdy, this being a new word with him, picked up in his first term at Dartmouth, and therefore to be used whenever possible for a while. Lester pronounced them 'bitchie', having still more recently acquired the term from an American art critic who had been staying with his parents. The Cottrells were evidently right in their contention that if introduced to it too early, children were likely to overlook the poetry of the Old Testament. Only the Quests were uninterested: they had had a religious housemaid for years, and brought up by servants, knew all that they wanted of the Bible.

'. . . for I'm S-A-V-E-D!' carolled Dru irrepressibly from *Wanderer* as we approached Ramsgate in the gathering dusk on the first lap of the return journey. I joined in from *Guadalupe*: by letting out our cut-down mainsail till it spilled the breeze we were sailing level with them as we reached towards the harbour, where we intended to spend the night. Father shouted at her irritably to go below and read out the harbour directions from *The Pilots' Guide*, partly to stop the hymn, partly to see how Mrs Cottrell took them, I imagine.

'The leading mark is the green light on the west cliff in line with the green light in the lighthouse,' she must have read (I could not hear her from the other boat, but I still know long passages of that discouraging book by heart). 'As there are no good clearing marks for the west side of the Brake Sound vessels should not attempt to work through Ramsgate Channel without local knowledge. *During night*, vessels should not attempt to run for Ramsgate, except in the event of extreme necessity.'

As the light faded from water and sky, Father shouted at us from the other boat to follow him in; we dropped behind and he sent someone forward to watch from *Wanderer*'s bow for the gleam of water breaking on the shoals near the entrance. Father explained to the anxious Mrs Cottrell, when the night thickened and no buoys were seen, that with a four-knot tide sluicing across the pier heads we could not sound-in slowly for fear of being swept on to the leeward jetty: it was a case of cracking on all sail and praying, while both boats rushed through the darkness towards what looked at the moment like a blank wall of cliff. Making the harbour was really nothing like as perilous as he allowed it to sound, with some characteristic idea of teaching Mrs Cottrell not to worry unduly.

And then Mrs Cottrell, to everyone's astonishment, turned adamant. She was not going to have her maternal heart agonised

again on this trip. She said that she did not care what we thought
of her or whose boats these were, we must go on up the coast, all
night if necessary: anything rather than attempt this dreadful
harbour in these dreadful conditions. A second and even greater
surprise followed: Father gave in to her courteously, having done
something with his head which Basil tried to convey to me
afterwards by reproducing the gesture. But one had to be Father to
carry off his mannerisms successfully: copied by a boy of eleven
that fling-back of the head and air of intense abstraction looked
theatrical. Father never did that: not to me, anyway. I could
remember, with something like awe, many occasions when I had
seen him start listening suddenly, as he must have done at that
moment, to something inaudible to other ears. The Cottrell children were travelling in *Guadalupe*, having come on board late that
morning, when the slow *Wanderer* had already started. Father
merely warned Mrs Cottrell that if it should come on to blow hard
(it was then, a trustworthy-looking night, and there seemed no
possibility of it) *Guadalupe*, having a partially new mainsail, would
not be able to reel: whatever happened she would have to carry on
with full canvas, because new cloths must be stretched by many
hours of sailing before they can safely be subjected to the uneven
strain of setting with a reef down. Was she prepared to accept that?

Yes, she was. Anything. Fierce winds were not an immediate
menace, like the black bulk of the cliffs ahead. She was not
frightened for herself in *Wanderer*, but she said again, a little
hysterically, that she was not going to have her children wrecked
in the smaller yacht in order that Father might show off his sailing
dexterity with this one.

Father signalled to us with a flash lamp to bear away and carry
on, and by the time that *Guadalupe* was clear of the foreland, we
began to think, not yet knowing the situation in the other boat,
that for once his sailing sense had deserted him. For how it blew!
A few minutes after we had turned away from the harbour a new
wind, a patchy little north-easterly, crept off the blackness of the
land and playfully pushed *Guadalupe*'s lee rail under water as an

earnest of what was to come. Marnie got her feet wet and was cross until she became too frightened to be cross. I have never known even a fisherman who could beat Father at smelling a wind before it came. How he must have enjoyed himself, in spite of the atmosphere of increasing hostility in his own boat, when it began to howl through the rigging as though summoned by his wish, and howled louder and louder all night.

Even the two Cottrells had to work at intervals, pumping out the water that came solid over *Guadalupe*'s low sides to swish about in the bilge, slopping up into the blanket locker and soaking most of the stores. There was no question of sleep for more than a few minutes at a time, towards morning, when we were all tired out. We lost touch with the other boat, and because of Sootie's orders about the accursed new canvas we dared not heave-to, which required reeling in this over-ardent boat.

In desperation we stood boldly but miserably out into the Worth Sea to get space enough in which to lower all the sails and ride to an improvised sea-anchor, waiting for daylight, while *Guadalupe* alternately stood on her nose and her counter, throwing in an occasional terrifying lurch and wallow as a sea broke aboard.

Margaret was very much Father's child that night. The channel always seems to be crowded with shipping when one is out in a small boat at night, and being run down was our only real danger, as Father knew: snuggled down to a sea-anchor *Guadalupe* could ride out a far heavier gale than this. With pride, with envy perhaps; with some such strong emotion in any case, I watched her standing under the port sidelight holding to the shrouds as the boat plunged, with the red light flickering over her wet face and wild, black, blowing hair, staring serenely at the dim bulk of an incoming steamer which was showing us both port and starboard lights. This meant that the ship was steering straight towards us, and because of the violence of our motion, our sidelights kept going out: we were not very visible in this welter of humped water without our white sails spread to catch whatever light there was. We should not be the first yacht to disappear hereabouts without trace if the steamer's look-out failed to see us. Margaret was not scared. She watched the approaching vessel with the same far-off air that sometimes maddened me because it seemed to me that, to look like this, she must have safe hold of something which I could never reach. But now it was a comforting thing, that calm expression on the queerly lit face. I was thoroughly scared myself, and clutching at straws of reassurance I thought—I felt without thinking rather— that loveliness like hers would be beyond the reach of danger from such ordinary things as ships and seas and winds. Surely anything so perfect must be safe. I was young enough to believe beauty enduring, and strong.

The ship saw us, in plenty of time really, and altered her course with a peevish blast from her siren. All night, tankers and tramps and Dover-bound continental packets passed uncomfortably close to us. Every hour or so, soaked to the skin in spite of their oilies, Sootie and Ronald came down into the cabin for a few minutes' rest out of the wind, but they could not leave the untrustworthy sidelights for long and it was essential to keep constant check of our position by cross-bearings on the North and South Foreland lights: if this north easterly veered at all we should be just to windward of the Goodwin Sands. Ronnie grumbled at Father as audibly as he thought safe in Sootie's hearing, expressing the blasphemous conviction that in his efforts to raise a tough family Father would do us all in, one of these days. And for once Sootie, who must have heard, did not shut him up loyally.

Father, in the other boat, had just the sort of night he enjoyed, hove-to under three reels in the lee of the Goodwins, occasionally taking short boards back into shelter when *Wanderer* drifted out towards rough water. He knew that we were safe from anything but bad luck: almost any boat can endure more than her crew: in ninety per cent of yachting accidents it is the human element that gives way; and Sootie and Ronald were hard-boiled enough to remain efficient through any ordinary gale. Mrs Cottrell, with whom Father was still very angry, did not know that: spiritually she must have had a much more wearing night in the steady old *Wanderer* than we did in *Guadalupe*.

Lester distinguished himself. Too shaken to be ill, he sat on the sodden bunk expressionlessly reading aloud, by the light of the wildly swinging lamp, remnants of old issues of *The Times*, which had swilled out of the lockers they had been used to line. This was the occasion on which he sowed his afterwards famous habit of producing solemn extracts from that paper at irrelevant moments, to emphasise his detachment from immediate cares. That night the Letters to the Editor shed on their subjects—bimetallism, Consular pensions or the first recorded appearance of potato blight in Dorset: I have forgotten what most of them were about—an ephemeral charm lacking from them in other circumstances. Their leisurely calm suggested a continuity of life which was very welcome just then. I even found myself trying to discuss them with Lester to make the time pass, while we listened apprehensively with three-quarters of our attention to the chaos outside the cabin. Years later, I came on one of these almost pulped pieces of paper in the pocket of a coat which had by then, in the usual way of family clothes, passed on to Margaret: 'Card Houses: It may interest some of your readers to know that I built a card house 26 storeys high, and have a photograph of it at 25 storeys. It took four packs of cards and was erected on a billiard table.—Mrs Fox, Tonbridge,' followed by 'Convolvulus Hawk Moth: A member of the Woodcote Park Golf Club near here recently found, on fencing near his house, a fine specimen of the Convolvulus Hawk Moth. The appearance of this rare moth so near London must be very exceptional.—Mr T. Lewis, Wallington.' This still seems to me the right sort of reading matter for gales: it encourages the belief that the importance of anything is a strictly relative matter. Lester and I agreed, for once, that it was difficult to imagine anyone reading it for choice when there was no gale on hand.

The weather stayed flithy all the next day, when we butted and rolled our way across the Thames estuary back to the familiar Suffolk waters.

69

As the last baton of us went ashore in the bobbing dinghy, Mother and Mrs Cottrell were brighter and more affable than ever, laughing as the spray flipped in. Mother said cheerily to us as we disembarked on the Hard, 'Well, children, that was great fun, wasn't it?' Lester and the Quests agreed, with courteous thanks, that it was. So did I.

I rushed to Ted Mawley for news of the now empty burrow. He told me that the heron's nest which we had been watering had been blown out of the elm on the edge of the Quests' garden and, piled up by the same raging north wind, the previous night's tide had risen far above the ordinary bird-tide level, sweeping the flats right up to the height of winter spring tides; it would be useless to look for nests now.

As soon as I heard this news, I was laid low by an agonising attack of conscience. I had told Mother a lie. I was not unnaturally truthful as a rule, but just occasionally the urge to righteousness won, as now, against my reluctance to confess anything to older people and so let them get at my mind. Driven by remorse, I went in search of Mother, whom I found lying down with a headache. Feeling almost as bad as I had done about my grandfather's death, I told her without any explanation that I had not enjoyed my treat at all. She sat up and stared at me. 'What did you say, Lallie?' I thought she was going to be cross. I repeated what I had said, awkwardly, wishing that I need not confess. Mother, that pillar of calm strength, burst into tears. It was by far the most harrowing moment of my childhood.

A LEE SHORE

John Scott Hughes

Rest after toil. Port after stormie seas.
Death after Life.
These things do greatlie please.

Here is a mystery. Why should army officers make better, or at lead more enthusiastic yachtsmen than officers of the navy? There are many distinguished exceptions, needless to say. But, cruising about, how frequently one meets General, or Colonel, Major, or Captain Somebody; how rarely an Admiral, Captain, or a Commander. If this is generally true, as it is in my own experience, possibly it is the result of the boat-*drill* to which youthful naval officers must submit; a dutiful exercise which, understandably, reacts ultimately, and the naval officer's choice moves in other directions from his early necessity. Perhaps this is a generalization altogether too sweeping. However that may be, it has been my own good fortune often to be shipmate with naval officers whose keenness was as great as their seamanly skill. Such is Murray. The best shipmate man ever had; patient, brave, imperturbable, cheerful always, and of wonderful stamina, and never have I known him lose his temper or his head—in this, Aye! and in other ways, so different to me!

Murray was often with me in my little *Puffin*. One night, the night off Lee—Is it not curious that many of the notoriously dangerous places round our coasts have names that are appropriately grim? The Manacles, The Casquets, The Shambles—no doubt one could compile a lengthy list.

Lee, however, as all who have sailed in the Solent know, scarcely deserves to be listed as one of the 'Dangers to Mariners'. It is not a rock-bound cliff fringed with terrors, but the mildest-looking bit of cliff in the world. Nevertheless, for Murray and me the name of this place will always have that forlorn sound associated with the words 'a lee shore'.

We chanced to be snugly moored at Bursledon, in the Hamble River, on the evening that Murray suggested making a night passage to Bembridge. That I should approve his proposal must be reckoned another triumph of hope over experience. There wasn't much wind. Distances at sea always seem longer by night. Bembridge is a difficult little place to enter, even by daylight. Moreover . . . But there is a romantic attraction about a night passage in a small vessel. In this instance, though, the glamour had rather a guilty tinge because we both of us were well aware that we should be better off where we were. The tide was foul, for one thing, and our boat was foul for another—sluggish through, being afloat months without a bottom-cleaning.

However, set out we did, under a cloudy night sky, but warm and almost oppressively still. The river banks were misty and hourly becoming less distinct. As we hauled the diminutive anchor home the cable made a noise that must have been audible far away inland. In some way the intense silence acted on our spirits; we really did feel as though this were a guilty escapade. We moved about stealthily, saying what had to be said in whispers. But once Murray, stubbing his naked toe against a cleat, spoke out loudly.

The easterly wind which had been blowing all day was now no more than enough to send the sails to sleep, as the saying is. This sufficed to keep us moving, though, yet so gently that the *Puffin*'s motion could only be assessed by the sudden appearance alongside, out of the blackness, of one 'boom' and then another.

Once outside the river there was not, of course, even this ghostly procession of the guiding booms to mark our progress. The only visible thing was a thin shaft of light from the cabin lamp. It seemed that we were hung motionless in some indistinguisable element, the water, the land, and the sky, all of the same degrees of soundless black. But presently, one by one, we picked up the lighted buoys and then the lightship, and then Lee light on the port bow, and at about the same time isolated flashes or winks of light along the Island shore. Our motion (if there was any) was unnoticeable, and we sprawled drowsily in the cockpit, too sleepy or too bewitched to break the silence.

Not long afterwards, after perhaps an hour of this drifting, I became aware of something odd. The light at the end of Lee pier had been our leading mark, and whoever was steering was supposed to keep it fine just on the port bow. But now there was no light.

Calling Murray's attention to this inexplicable thing, I held forth indignantly on the scandal it was that so important a light, in the Solent of all places, was not watched or automatically controlled or something. My companion was not to be shocked, however, or even impressed; I don't think he was even interested.

'Oh, I suppose the gas has escaped, or something like that,' said Murray, yawning. 'Why should anybody have to stay awake to see such a potty little light doesn't go out? I'm a bit sleepy myself. Suppose we have a watch below? I'll go first,' he added quickly.

I was left alone in the cockpit to ponder on the mystery of the lights of Lee. It was certainly strange. Just now, from my position at the unresponsive tiller, I could look out on a great expanse of unlighted waters. From time to time the Warner lightship glowed on the eastern horizon, and somewhere away on our starboard quarter the Prince Consort buoy was flashing with soporific regularity. There were, in addition, one or more lesser lights in that direction, but, so far as I could recall, they held no significance for the mariner. In brief, when I say unlighted waters, what I mean is to all intents and purposes—or rather for the intent and purpose of coaxing a small yacht past the cliffs of Lee—we were, literally, sailing in the dark.

Sitting there alone in the cockpit with the tiller tucked under my arm I fell to thinking how lonely is the sea, how hazardous can be this game of sailing, even on so disciplined and orderly a sheet of water as the Solent ... You would have thought that there would have been at least one late-to-bed householder whose light would have signified the existence of that dark cliff that was undoubtedly there, yonder somewhere, away to port in the dark. But there wasn't. Not one. On so still a night, you would have thought, we might have heard the sound of surf on the shingle beach. But I couldn't. Not a murmer.

Yet we seemed to be moving through the water; I could hear a constant little ripple round the bows. No doubt much of this apparent motion was due to the tide, for our sails were still, and so must be holding some breath of wing. And I would have given something just then to know how much tide there was. Were we making any headway at all? Possibly. But if so, the far-off lights on the other side of the Solent gave no clue, for I could not notice that their bearings altered perceptibly. Meanwhile, just where were we?

Time stood still. I nodded at the tiller. Now and then I started up with the resolve to call Murray. But why call him? Murray, that placid soul, fresh from slumber, would not have remained awake for a moment—where was the need, in this uncanny uninhabited world of silence, this night Sargasso of the Solent? I could not have said to him 'Steer so-and-so', since, short of pushing her into the strength of the tide, there was nothing to do but to carry on where we were—wherever that might be. Dawn must soon break, and then we should see—

CRASH! *Bump-bump-bump!*

I was flung against the forward end of the cockpit. As the yacht swung off in a wide arc, a bright light shone full on us from overhead, a bright hazy light ruddy in the mist. Murray stumbled out of the cabin, 'Lord! What's that?'

'Lee,' I told him. 'Lee pier.'

THE FRENCH NUDIST & ME

Kay Cartwright

The man who would be fully employed should procure a
ship or a woman for no two things produce more trouble.

Not knowing what lay ahead, and having only romantic notions
about the sea, I married a sailing enthusiast. After four years of
exhaustive feminine strategy and a half-way-around-the-world
chase, I had finally captured this Texan. I figured that everything
from now on must be downhill, even crossing the Atlantic in a 38
foot yawl named *Scuffler*, which was to be my new home. I bought
a book on knots and prepared to become a fantastic first mate;
visions of the two of us, alone, brave and intrepid, battling the
elements, ran rampant through my brain. How wrong I was!

Jerry and I set sail from Falmouth, England, on a clear sunny
day. I took the wheel feeling rather full of myself. There didn't
seem to be much to this sailing. Two days later in the throes of a
force ten gale, I had a much clearer picture. If not lashed down, I
was hurled, violently about the cabin. The wind screamed and
howled in the rigging, and it seemed our small boat could not
possibly survive. What a ghastly way to go! Jerry was leaning over
the stern with a strange canvas contraption attached to a rope
which he planned to trail behind us to slow *Scuffler* down.

'Shouldn't we send up flares?' I yelled frantically.

'The boat can take anything this storm can give us, we're OK,'
he shouted back.

Madness, I decided. Marriage must have driven him to some sort
of death wish.

I had not stowed the boat properly. An assortment of food, tin cans, rice and sugar tumbled out onto the cabin sole where they crashed and slopped back and forth. We were wet, cold, and in any case, very seasick. Clutching the bucket, dressing in long johns, copious sweaters, and oilskins—an utterly sexless, dejected object—I clung to the canvas lee-boards and prayed for rescue.

As if to emphasize this nightmare situation, a calm, detached BBC voice spoke from our radio, giving the weather forecast for our area, and predicting gales for the next 24 hours. Didn't he know or care that we were out here? He ended with 'Goodnight, gentlemen, and good sailing.' *This*, I decided, is what cruising is all about, and I've had a horror of the sailing part of it ever since.

Miles later, after many, to my way of thinking, terrifying adventures, I was still somehow on board. I had discovered life in harbour on a boat could be enormous fun, but as far as sailing went, I remained completely unseaworthy. Horace, a Spanish alley cat we had acquired in a bar, was now the first mate.

The day before the dreaded Atlantic crossing finally arrived, I was sitting on deck gazing longingly at the land and bracing myself for the worst, when I noticed a small figure with a great quantity of long blonde hair rowing by. It was 4 p.m. and, being British to the last, I invited her aboard for a cup of tea. Her name was Rosemary Brubella. She was French, and quite charming. She was also a very keen sailor, travelling complete with her own sextant and rubber dinghy. These had been rescued, it seemed, from her boat which had been wrecked off the Portuguese coast.

All this impressed me very much. It became apparent by the second cup of tea that Rosie would like to join us on *Scuffler*. She was a journalist and wanted to write stories about the Caribbean. I asked her if she could cook, my batting average in the galley at sea being rather poor. With an expressive wave of her hand she said, 'I am French, of course I cook!' Jerry, sitting behind her, was nodding at me enthusiastically, and so Rosie joined our crew. The next day we set sail for Barbados.

For the first three days the sky was grey and we were pushed by the winds towards the coast of Africa. I clung grimly to my bucket and just succeeded in doing my watches. Rosie, enveloped in huge oilskins, leapt cheerfully about, hauling in sails and heaving on winch handles. She also did wonderful things in the galley, swinging wildly on the rope attaching her life harness to the grab rail above the stove, humming a tune, and rummaging in a paper bag which contained 101 spices, a part of her kit she was apparently never without. She produced gourmet meals. Rosie was obviously going to be a great crew member.

The fourth day out, I crawled out of my bunk, where I had been dreaming as usual of drowning, and thought I would go up on deck for some air. We had a following wind and the sun was shining as *Scuffler* barrelled along under twin jibs. My gaze fell on the foredeck and remained riveted. Rosie, sitting on a towel and soaking up the sun, had absolutely no clothes on. I was quite amazed, probably a fault of my English upbringing. I hopped quickly back down below, and pointing a rather shaky finger forward, said to Jerry, 'Have you seen . . .'

'Sure,' he said cheerfully. 'People always take all their clothes off at sea.'

'Well, I'm not,' I said stiffly. 'Couldn't pass the physical.' And made myself some tea—a great stand-by in the hour of need.

After some thought I decided that wearing no clothes was probably quite healthy and normal; there is nothing disgraceful about the human body. I resolved to approach the thing with a more open mind, and popped back on deck for a chat with Rosie. I found her scribbling away in her notebook.

'What are you writing?' I asked.

'I used to write ze romantic story,' she said with a smile. 'Now I write ze erotic one.'

I retreated below once again to make more tea, this time adding a dash of whisky.

'Trapped,' I thought. 'On a space 10′ x 38′ with a French nudist who writes erotic books. And no one can get off.' This was not the honeymoon I had envisaged.

The weather continued, fair. We had following winds, and

Scuffler was sailing well, steering herself under twin jibs. This relieved the situation whereby one of us had to be clamped to the wheel at all times, and was a great joy. About this time Jerry also decided to abandon his clothes and leap about with nothing on.

He used the good weather to give Rosie navigating lessons, the two of them poring over the chart table, working out sights. The conversation was all about transit lines, hour angles, assumed positions, and quite beyond me. I did feel, however, that it didn't fit in with the two bare bottoms perched on the engine housing.

Being the only non-sailor aboard, I refrained from comment. Seafaring people obviously led a simple, natural life, their minds circling free and clear above convention. I hoped that at no time would their minds sink to more earthly thoughts.

This situation was soon relieved when Jerry got badly sunburned in a quite agonizing way and had to leap smartly back into his swimming trunks. I laughed hilariously and received very black looks. Rosie, however, continued on her naked way although I did manage to persuade her to wrap a sarong around her middle during meals, not being quite able to cope with the naked body and gourmet food at the same time.

Our fresh water was only used for drinking and cooking, and Rosie, child of nature that she was, used to take showers on deck every time it rained, scrubbing herself all over a small stiff brush until bright pink and red. Too spartan for me: I abstained.

But Jerry usually joined her and, clutching his soap and brush, the two of them would scrub and cavort about in the cockpit, faces lifted to the rain like pagan creatures. At times like this, I would gaze at Horace in disbelief. He would blink in his smug cat-like way, and sometimes to my addled brain seemed to be smiling.

In the evenings with the boat steering herself, Jerry attempted to play the guitar and Rosie sang and made music by beating on the bottom of a saucepan. I kept my end up, as they say in England, and we all drank wine. And so *Scuffler* with her strange crew, bravely churned her way across the Atlantic.

Fourteen days out of Las Palmas we ran into squalls and

headwinds. Our twin jibs had to be abandoned and we were back on watches. We seemed to be changing sails constantly. Jerry and Rosie worked on the foredeck and handled the winches while I, being considered completely unsafe out of the cockpit, took the wheel. Great screaming matches usually accompanied these sessions using nautical language which I didn't understand, and bad language which I did.

'Head her up into the wind, fall off, hold her steady—goddam dumb broad.' These happy times usually ended with Rosie or Jerry seizing the wheel from me in a fury and managing to steer with one hand, using the other hand, teeth and/or feet to handle winches and grasp sheets in fantastic acts of seamanship while I was asked to simply 'keep out of the way'.

What had happened to those great dreams of me as first mate— Jerry's right arm as we bravely battled the elements together? When I did my watch, Jerry always insisted on tying my lifeline himself, not trusting my rather exotic knots—the final insult, considering the book on knots I had bought during that time of early enthusiasm. In this way, I was firmly lashed for the duration of my stay out there, with thoughts of the luscious Rosie languishing below.

People have suggested to me that this was all highly suspicious. However, I honestly think Jerry was simply ensuring that I would not be carried away by a large wave and left stranded in an unfriendly sea. At times on watch, wet, cold, and buffeted, I found, myself screaming at the sea, 'I hate you!' Jerry, catching me in the act, was convinced that I should have to be off-loaded for the funny farm immediately upon arrival in Barbados. Maybe this was another reason he felt it necessary to tie me down.

The weather was worsening and the seas building up. We had strong headwinds and some really bad squalls. And the barometer was dropping. Jerry began to think of hurricanes and we checked with the British Admiralty Pilot. It said something helpful about getting up steam in all boilers and preparing to take avoiding action if the barometer dropped below five millibars. Our barometer had dropped nine. I gazed in disbelief at our temperamental 10 h.p. petrol engine. It knew nothing of avoiding actions. We abandoned the British Pilot.

Within a few hours the sky was heavy with black clouds, and a brilliant lightning storm flashed and thundered about us. I felt that our mast must be the only thing sticking up for miles and that we would inevitably be struck at any moment. We were now lying a-hull under bare poles, the boat rolling violently in a ghastly see-saw motion. I was lashed into my bunk, clutching the bucket as usual. Rosie was not singing and Horace was not smiling.

Jerry went up on deck where he half-inflated the life-raft, and got supplies ready in case we should be forced to abandon *Scuffler*. He also put a pair of bolt cutters in a handy place in case we should be dismasted and need to cut the mast free from the rigging. All these activities only served to increase my horror. I leaned weakly from my bunk and said, 'My God, Rosie, we're not going to make it.' To be cheated having endured so much!

'We just 'ave to be prepared,' she said. 'My poor petite Kay, I will make something for you. It will give you strength'; and she fluttered obediently towards the galley where she stirred and hummed over a survival brew. The answer it seems, for the French, always lies in the stomach.

My mother had predicted rescue by helicopter from the very beginning of this expedition. But did anyone know we were out here? We had no ship-to-shore radio; Jerry didn't want one aboard. At best I could see the three of us and Horace washed up on some desert island, Rosie wearing only a flower in her hair, building a straw house, and cooking over the camp fire with her 101 spices. This honeymoon could go on for ever!

High winds, intermittent rain which came down in sheets, and lightning storms stayed with us for a week. *Scuffler* ploughed through under bare poles or storm jib, and we lived in wet oilskins and took shorter watches. At night, surrounded by inky blackness and the screaming wind, the only thing visible in the cockpit was the compass light.

Rosie behaved *magnificently*, helping Jerry on the foredeck at great danger to life and limb, the two of them often airborne as *Scuffler* dropped off the huge waves. By the end of the week we felt as if we had lived for ever in this wet, violent world and we stopped looking at the barometer. Sometimes Rosie would tap it as she went by and swear 'Merde!' to herself in French. I thought if only I could be allowed to get out of this alive, I would be good for ever.

The weather gradually improved and the great crunch never came. We later discovered that we had been in the southern quadrant of a late October hurricane running parallel to us as it recurved easterly. Once again *Scuffler* bowled along under twin jibs.

Rosie sang, happy to be out of the confines and fetters of clothes, and did wonderful things in the gallery with her spice bag. I tried to persuade her that cooking on a boat in the unclothed state can be hazardous to your health, but to no avail.

Horace was eating all the flying fish that hit the deck, and was sailing again. Jerry tried to play the guitar, and I lurched about with my bucket. Life had returned to normal.

Barbados was by now only a few days away and Rosie decided the time had come to give her wardrobe a once-over. Surprised that she had a wardrobe, I sat fascinated, as two large suitcases were dragged into the cabin. I had wondered all along what these suitcases could possibly contain. Manuscripts of rare and erotic verse perhaps?

The lids were flung back and the cases seemed to be full of boots and shoes and the odd sarong. Most curious. Then from some dark, corner she pulled out a long back net-like contraption.

Thinking this must be Rosie's patent fishing net which accompanied her on all her travels along with the dinghy and the spice bag, I was amazed to see it had legs and arms, and even more amazed to see Rosie climbing into it. The thing, covering her nude body from neck to wrist to ankles, was made up of holes about one inch across.

Dressed to kill, she whirled gaily about the cabin, doing some sort of modern ballet. To me it looked quite obscene. I thought the old Rosie looked far nicer with nothing on at all, which shows how far I had progressed in my thinking! I seemed to need constant resuscitation these days and put the kettle on for tea.

We had been at sea 28 days and Jerry, frustrated at his lack of success at fishing, finally hooked a pair of my red panties onto his line. Within minutes it seemed, the line was taut and straining. We had hooked a big one. Jerry and Rosie heaved on the line in a fever of excitement while I squealed hysterically from the cabin.

'Cut it loose, don't kill it! It was happy before we arrived.' I hated to see anything killed.

Ignoring me, they continued to pull furiously. A silver shape appeared and then the head broke the surface—Jerry had hooked a barracuda! The fish lurched and fought the line, his jaws gaping wide and vicious.

'Cut the line,' I screamed. 'I can't stand it!'

This time Jerry and Rosie obeyed, not because the fish had been happy out there, but because they didn't want to lose the odd finger or perhaps an arm to the snapping jaws, and Rosie wasn't sure about it being good to eat. Another traumatic episode in the voyage was over, and I refused to allow any more of my underwear to be used as a lure.

We were almost there and spirits were up. That night I looked out of the aft hatch to admire the beautiful tropical night and saw Rosie hanging from the backstay, silhouetted against the moon, one foot resting on top of the wheel and doing some sort of interpretative dance. She was nude as usual and singing one of her strange French songs. Horace, sitting on the cockpit seat, was gazing up at her in admiration. Not wanting to break the spell, I crawled back into my bunk with a hot toddy, and tried to work it all out.

At 5 a.m., 29 days out of Las Palmas, a grey line appeared on the horizon—Barbados at last, and we had made it. I couldn't believe it. The line grew until finally there were trees and houses. My relief and gratitude were enormous.

As we entered the harbour Rosie, wrapped in a sarong and looking extremely chaste, went forward to get the anchor ready to run. Friends we had known in Las Palmas were rowing over to greet us with large rum punches and they looked in amazement at the small figure with masses of golden hair wrestling with the anchor chain.

'Who's that?' was the first question.

'That,' I said, 'is Rosie,' and left it. All, I felt sure, would soon be revealed.

We could not clear Customs that day as it was Sunday. However, our friends piled illegally on board with their rum punches and by the afternoon we were all three sheets to the wind. Rosie had long since flung aside her sarong and was massaging some lucky skipper's back. She had evidently studied massage as well as modern ballet at some stage.

Later that day we all dived into the harbour and swam over to a larger boat. In her usual state of undress, Rosie proceeded to cook for about 20 people. By the end of the evening it seemed quite a few of the girls were running around topless.

'This Caribbean is really something!' Jerry said with obvious enthusiasm.

The next morning we woke up on *Scuffler* with very little idea how we got back. Gazing in a bleary fashion out of the hatch, Jerry noticed the Customs boat making for us at a fast clip and we didn't have Rosie on board to be accounted for. We screamed over to the boat that had been the scene of the night's activities and she was swiftly delivered to us wrapped in a sheet, protesting loudly, 'But vere are my clothes?'

For some reason the Customs decided to overlook these odd goings-on, and by the time they had climbed aboard, Rosie sat present and correct, smiling demurely in her sheet. The Customs men seemed to be so enchanted by her that they completely failed to notice Horace, who was marching boldly about between their feet. We had officially arrived.

After a few days in Barbados, Rosie flew on to Grenada to meet friends from another boat. Although I was too shattered to appreciate it at the time, she had been good fun and good crew, and certainly an experience. My great Atlantic crossing honeymoon had not gone to plan. In fact, I planned no more such voyages.

We went on to cruise the Caribbean for six months and towards the end knew we had achieved a small measure of cruising fame when someone would look up as we entered a new harbour and say . . .

'*Scuffler*, oh yes, you're the boat that brought Rosie across.

HAPPY ENDING

Alfred F. Loomis

Blow, blow, thou winter wind,
Thou art not so unkind
As Man's ingratitude.

William Shakespeare, As You Like It

I met Tommy Wiley for the first time on the French coast, off the shifting entrance to Trouville. The tide was at the top of the flood, all but turned, the wind was slight, and as I didn't want to be locked out of the wet basin, I was entering under power. Ahead of me I saw a lovely cutter—not one of your old-fashioned type, which are beautiful in their ruggedness, but a racing boat, slender, low of hull, tall of rig, gracefully proportioned for speed. She was finished bright, and in the warm sunlight her pine deck and mahogany sides seemed to lend a creamy glow to the rippling whiteness of her sails. Coming to the western edge of the narrow channel she tacked and slowly gathered way on the other board. There I overtook her and was passing with a silent wave when her helmsman called across the almost breathless water:

'Are you a stranger here, *Swastika*?' (*Swastika* being the name of my yawl.)

'Yes,' I returned. 'Am I standing into danger?'

'You'd, better leave the next black buoy to starboard,' he replied. 'It's fifty yards out of position.'

I had idled my motor at his first word, and now had so little headway that the two yachts drew together. 'Thanks,' said I. 'I'd probably have gone aground. Can I return the favour by towing you in?'

85

Wiley looked aloft at his towering spread of canvas, cast a calculating glance at the lock gates perhaps a quarter-mile away, and gently shook his head. 'I think I can make it,' he declared. 'The element of uncertainty doubles the enjoyment.'

'Well,' said I, dubiously, for the wind was very light and dead ahead . . . 'See you inside.' And I motored in.

I had been moored in the Deauville basin for at least twenty minutes when I stepped to the gates to see how the element of uncertainty was coming on. *Thalassa*—I had read her name in passing and looked up her ownership in Lloyd's—was again on the starboard tack, inside the jetties, but seemingly bound up-channel for Trouville. The current had begun its ebb. The wetted surface of the lock gates which betrayed the falling tide was at least four inches wide and growing fast. The uniformed guards by the gates silently watched the diminishing water, apparently oblivious of the yacht's manoeuvres. When the level reached a certain mark they would close the basin whether one or a dozen boats remained outside. They had to, for the safety of those moored within.

As the minutes passed and the water subsided I became unable to curb my impatience. 'Are you coming in?' I called. 'Shall I tell them to wait for you.'

'They won't,' Wiley calmly answered. 'I think I'll do the trick.'

As he neared the south side of the narrow harbour he came about, heading a hundred yards high of the gates, no more than twenty yards between his fragile bow and the solid masonry of the retaining wall. I saw at once that for each foot he forged ahead the ebb current carried him a yard to the westward, and admired Wiley for the closeness of his calculations. If a sudden puff had caught his sails he might have come to grief. But he discounted that contingency.

Perhaps three minutes had passed when the French guards began to lose their immobility. They exchanged words and motioned with their hands to supplement their conversation. But as yet they made no move toward closing the gates. I stood transfixed, willing *Thalassa* to hurry in; and if mind had true supremacy over matter

86

she would have leaped forward, torpedo-like. Instead she drifted slowly downstream, ever slightly nearer.

The moment came when I, by leaning out, could have placed my hand on *Thalassa*'s bow, and I made as if to do so. But Wiley stopped me. 'Give her another minute by herself,' said he, 'That will put her inside, I might get a little puff.'

I restrained myself and the seconds dragged on. The puff came. The cutter, heeling slightly, seemed to gather herself like a bay mare before slipping inside.

'Voilà,' said one guard, unemphatically, as he closed his gate some eight or nine inches astern of *Thalassa*.

'Bravo,' rejoined the other, with somewhat more feeling.

When the gates joggled together I ran across and came up alongside the cutter at the west side of the basin.

Wiley was putting the boom rest into place as his two paid hands made fast the mooring lines, 'Lower away,' said he, and turned toward me. 'If they had closed the gates in my face I would have drifted out with the stream and sailed on to Le Havre. It wasn't a matter of life and death.'

I stepped aboard to help lower sail, and marked that he worked with extreme deliberation. It was not the deliberation of a lazy man or of one mentally slow. Rather it was the cautious movement of one who has schooled himself to avoid violence of gesture. Later when he asked me below to have a drink and begged me to excuse him from participating, I jumped to a conclusion. 'A yachtsman who doesn't drink?' I asked. 'It seems hardly proper.'

'It's my heart, you know,' said he, apologetically. 'Got a bit of shrapnel near it during the war, and I have to take things easy.'

With the picture of his calm, leisurely entrance vivid in my mind I was ready for the moment to believe that he could always take things easily aboard *Thalassa*. But then I had another image of such a racing boat bouncing in the short Channel sea, and I exclaimed, 'Surely, man, you don't think sailing is good for the heart!'

He laughed. 'I'm not easily frightened to death, if that's what you mean, and if it comes on to blow I have two excellent hands who do the heavy work. *Thalassa* steers like a witch. At such times I chock myself off in the cockpit, take the helm, and I haven't a thing to worry me. Fortunately, yachting is the only sport for a man with my diaphanous attachment to life. I say 'fortunately', because all other sports bore me to extinction.'

That evening Wiley accompanied me aboard to supper and we revealed our differing cruising philosophies and techniques in mutual tolerance and understanding. My preference is to go on and on to new waters—his, he told me, was to explore each harbour thoroughly, to know the coast under all conditions of wind and tide, to feel as much at home on the sea as his *Thalassa*, which was named for it. I need not add that he was wedded to sail and tiller and entertained complete contempt for anything that was rotary in its movement.

It was the next year, I think, that I saw Tommy Wiley again. Once more I was entering under power—this time at Dieppe—and I own to a twinge of shame when he saw me with my sails furled. He sat in the stern sheets of a mahogany skiff, a uniformed sailor at the oars moving him from place to place as he took soundings with a three-pound lead. Later, when the tide lifted and I passed through the Pollet draw to find mooring in the Duquesne basin, Wiley came in after me and accepted my invitation to step aboard.

As if to set my mind at rest he began by telling me that Dieppe was one haven, what with Channel packets coming and going, at which he always took a tow. And he hoped (somewhat to my surprise) that we might go out together so that if I felt disposed he could be spared a fee. I told him that I would suit my departure to his.

'Now that that's settled, ' I added, 'will you kindly tell me what treasure you expected to pick up with your lead from the polluted floor of Dieppe?'

He seated himself carefully in a chair which I had had brought for him on deck, and humorously shrugged his shoulders. I was doing that,' said he, 'to get away from my paying guests. They

88

wanted me to come to this port, and in a way I had to. But I'm dashed if I have to caper about with them ashore.'

He sat with his chair turned so that he faced *Thalassa*, moored a hundred yards or so from us, and I noticed that his eyes continually caressed her lovely hull and lofty mast.

'Isn't this a new departure?' I asked, 'Guests on *Thalassa*? I thought you liked going your own gait.'

'I do. More now than I did a year ago. These are *paying* guests.' He paused a moment and continued in the best counterfeit of an offhand manner that he could assume. 'The fact is I've had terrific financial reverses. I can't afford the cutter. I can't give her up. I would die ashore. So to make both ends meet I have to take these guests. They're good fellows, you know, but they don't love the sea as I do, and I have to get away from them from time to time. By the way, do you think this makes me a professional?'

'You, a professional!' I hooted. 'An amateur is one who loves something. If you love *Thalassa* enough to share her rather than give her up altogether—or, looking at it from another angle, if you're so keen about sailing that you will endure the embarrassments of paying guests rather than stay ashore—I think you are doubly an amateur.'

Nevertheless, I reflected uncomfortably that in the opinion of those who really matter, Wiley's amateur status had been impaired.

Our third meeting, a year later, occurred in the Channel south of the English port of Newhaven. I had noticed a sailing dinghy scooting along, her helmsman immovable at the tiller, head back and eyes unwavering on the luff of his sail. Calm overtook us and I launched my skiff, rowing over for a talk with the intrepid stranger.

'Wiley!' I exclaimed, graping his gunwale and fending off. 'Where's *Thalassa*?'

'This is she,' he replied gravely. 'You hadn't heard that my other boat was burned at Bembridge just after I had hauled her out last fall?'

'I heard about the fire,' I replied, 'but *Thalassa*—that dream of beauty.'

Our two small boats lifted leisurely to the heave of the sleeping sea. 'Perhaps it was for the best,' said Wiley stoically. 'I—well, I had been expelled from my club for professionalism—you know, those paying guests—and I doubt if I could have gone on with her. Now I live in a room by the sea at Newhaven and sail this little dream of beauty—again an amateur, I hope. I make no comparisons with my old love, but I feel a more intimate companionship with the sea in this 14-footer than I ever did before.'

He said nothing of the shock of his loss or of his expulsion from the fellowship of Corinthians, but, scanning his face, I could see that he had definitely aged. I asked no questions, other than the routine one of, 'Have you been caught in anything dirty?'

'Yes, but I've been able to run for it. And you ought to see her off the wind.' His grave face brightened vividly. He held out a hand, palm down, and oscillated it slightly from the wrist. 'Like that,' said he. 'A marble on her thwart would hardly roll six inches from side to side. Oh, marvellous!'

'Your heart?' I asked. 'Does it give you any trouble.'

'No more than usual. I'm no weakling, you know,' he boasted. 'I can reef, haul, and steer with the best of you, so long as I take things easily.'

I asked Wiley if he intended to lie there becalmed all night, and he elected to think my question facetious. 'There will be wind before dark. Plenty of it. Where are you bound?'

'Newhaven,' said I, at random. 'If the wind is west it will be a close reach in.'

'And a close squeak for boats that aren't weatherly.'

'As bad as that?' I asked. 'Say, wouldn't you like me to bring over the yawl and tow you a bit? Not in, but to weather a mile or so.'

He looked toward the distant shore, marked at that moment by the smoke of a steamer leaving Newhaven. 'No thanks, I ought to make it.'

'Then, how about tying in a reef while I'm here. Wouldn't that help?'

'No, I'll need whole sail for the first hour or so, and perhaps I shan't have to reef at all.'

The first darkening of the water to westward now became apparent. Expressing a final wish that I could do something to assist Wiley, I rowed back to my *Swastika* and boarded her as the wind came in. The meeting had been a pleasant one, for, rising above his personal misfortunes, Wiley had suffused me afresh with his love of sailing. I found myself thinking fatalistically that if (or rather, when) he did overtax his heart in some such exigency as this approaching westerly he would die happy.

As I gathered way, *Thalassa* glided past me and I noticed how much at union with his boat this sailor was—stretched at ease, one arm thrown carelessly along the tiller, head just showing above the gunwale, and face uplifted so that his eyes commanded the luff of his sail. After nodding to me he looked to westward and nodded his head more emphatically, as if to say, 'I told you so.'

A moment later he looked back and called, 'Better get your skiff aboard. This will be quick.'

I thought him unduly anxious—as well he might be in an open boat—and left my skiff towing. Because of my neglect I was unable to watch some two hours later when the time came for him to reef. In the interval the wind had shot up to gale force and the slumbering sea had leaped to tumultuous, vicious life. What with heaving to to lower my mainsail, and inexcusably sagging down and overriding my skiff, my men and I had the busiest half hour of our experience. When they had righted the skiff and manhandled it aboard I had time to look around and see how Wiley had managed. He, too, was shortened down, and although his boat seemed to skip bodily from crest to crest he told me afterward that she made remarkably easy weather of it.

Swastika readied port first, and I was in readiness to receive him as he came careering up the narrow harbour. Though he made an eggshell landing alongside my yawl, he depended on us to secure him and lower his wildly slatting sail. And one of my men and I had to lift him bodily to my deck and below to a bunk.

91

'I did it that time,' was all he would say of his experience at sea. I inferred that he spoke of his heart rather than of his feat of seamanship, for he added, 'Looks like a spell with the doctor.'

The next day we got him ashore and to his own room, where a doctor stethoscoped him and made other tests. His verdict—bed, and no more sailing—brought a look of profoundest gloom to Wiley's face. I stayed in port several days, visiting the sick man frequently. When, finally, I left, it was with his assurance that he was well cared for and that he would obey the doctor's orders and do nothing rash.

'The fact is,' he told me, 'I *feel* weak for the first time since I left the base hospital. This damned heart of mine, you know has what they call a pericardial adhesion and has to turn itself upside down every time it pumps. It may knock off work any minute.'

I returned after two weeks, blithely expecting, as a well man does, to find Wiley recovered. But there was a wasted look to his face that took my breath away. Out of bed, but confined to his room, almost his first words expressed his repugnance to life ashore.

'I feel like a sick bear in a cage,' said he, 'padding about, wall to wall, bed to eating tray. If I could have a little sail on a calm day it would give me new life. But I haven't had quite the gumption to slip out against the doctor's orders.'

'That's right,' I counselled him. 'Obey orders and build up slowly.'

He turned savagely upon me. 'But what's the use?' he asked. 'If I stay in this hole I'll die. Sailing always does me good. If this wind would only let up!'

Although the vagaries of Channel weather are unpredictable by me, there seemed little chance of that. In the last week the wind had blown half a gale for five days and a whole gale for the other two. The sea pounded on the shore until it rattled the windows of the sick man's room. The wind howled down his chimney and puffed wisps of dead ashes out of the black grate.

'As for me,' said I, 'I'm quite content to be in port.'

But that night the wind died. I awoke in the morning full of the joy of sunshine. In the leftover swell finding its way into the harbour the moored boats still rolled reminiscently, but the surface of the water was flecked by the gentlest of winds from the north-east. I looked out of the main hatch to see who had come and gone. Early though it was, *Thalassa*'s mooring was empty.

I jumped into my skiff, and ashore, and ran full tilt to the lighthouse on the west pier, still damp from its bath of spray. Far to sea I saw a leg-of-mutton sail, slowly dwindling.

Full of misgivings, I returned aboard for breakfast and by an effort of will resisted the temptation to put after the afflicted man. Though his heart was weak his weather sense was still strong and I convinced myself that he would not get caught out a second time. All that lovely summer day I loitered at the harbour mouth, watching the shipping and ever turning an anxious glance to sea. At last I saw him coming from the west, sailing on an easy reach. As he drew near I could distinguish him in his familiar pose, arm thrown carelessly along the tiller, head showing above the gunwale, eyes on the luff of the sail. When he came nearer still I saw that the luff shook slightly and that *Thalassa*'s course was not arrow-straight.

Before I had time to digest the significance of this, a deep-throated whistle blistered my ear drums and I looked around to see the Dieppe steamer charing out from her wharf. At full speed almost before she reached the entrance, she was giving all lesser craft the signal to keep clear. I looked again at *Thalassa*. What was she going to do, skim across the steamer's bow, or luff up and pass astern? A careful seaman would, of course, have passed astern, but I remembered Wiley's delight in his calculation of clearances when first I saw him at Trouville. *Thalassa* held to her course, clearing the packet's knife-like bow by a distance measurable in feet rather than in yards. I saw her stern rise to the bow wave, and just before the black hull of the steamer intervened I thought I saw Wiley put her about for the entrance.

It was my next thought that he had cut his distance so close that the steamer had run him down. But in a few seconds *Thalassa* reappeared, almost shaving the steamer's stern, and bobbing in her wake. She straightened up and on the starboard tack entered the harbour, the tide under her. A thrill of admiration tingled me as I saw that Wiley's nonchalance remained superb. He did not once look astern at the black death that had so narrowly escaped him.

The wind by now was almost gone (getting ready for another week of southwesterlies, I thought) and it was more by the indulgence of tide than air that *Thalassa* drifted slowly to her mooring. But Wiley, sailor that he was, still kept his glance riveted to the luff of his sail.

Running ahead to my skiff I jumped in and shoved off. *Thalassa* sailed serenely on until her bow actually kissed her mooring buoy. Then, though, she seemed to hesitate an instant, she kept on.

Speechless, I rowed alongside and touched Wiley's arm where it lay carelessly along the tiller. Its coldness was communicated through the coat sleeve to my fingers. I looked at the lifeless face and saw that though the eyes were open the mouth was closed, the corners of the lips just lifting to a smile.

'God!' I whispered, 'If we could all go out as happily as that.'

THEY WALK BY NIGHT

J.D.S.

From *Blackwoods*

Sailing offshore means you're going to spend a lot of time sitting in the dark. Ideally, on passage, you should be able to allow the routine of the watches, sleep and duty, sleep and duty to flow evenly on through daylight and dark. In fact, the coming of night is all too often the signal for noble feats of endurance and a lot of nocturnal bobbings about with nourishing snacks every half-hour.

If you have had the sense to get your head down during daylight and unless you are hog-tied by habit and can only sleep when the cat has been put out, the night will only be a more peaceful continuation of the day. Some people seem incapable of doing a night watch without commotion. The eternal creeping around down below, rummaging under sleepers for gear, the deafening whispers and the periodical loud voice raised on the wind which has every sleeper sitting bolt upright grabbing for his pants are essential to a night watch for them. You hear: 'There it is—No—I can't—I—two spoons,' or some such gibberish and you must lie there for the next half-hour grimly trying to get to sleep again.

It seems the people who get all anxious about sleep are the ones who end by getting the least. On the first night out it is hard to store up hours of sleep during the preceding daylight. You can lie down for a watch and read quietly, but the grim little faces we see with eyelids screwed up tight like little steamed puddings, lurking under their blankets, are a joke.

By midnight and after, you can go down to a sound four hours' gonk and benefit by it and if you still don't want to sleep, so what? It's the *next* night that catches people out and by then it's a bad case that hasn't slept at all. The big enemy is the sunshine to us poor wizened, sun-starved islanders. We thrust our poor little white pans up to the sun like daisies and the idea of going down into the gloom for a sleep is repellent. 'I'll go out on the foredeck,' we say, 'I'll sleep there instead.' Do we hell.

Try to get a good forenoon nap and another evening one. Allowing for meals and general monkeying about with sails, this will add up to five or six hours, maybe, and that plus another four during the night is enough for anyone. Worst enemy of sleep when the watch below is half gone on other things is this 'I *must* drop off. I've only got an hour and a half left' attitude. Better to get the book out and just rest. Ten to one you'll wake up dribbling on the first page.

On the whole, most folk prefer long daylight watches and short ones at night. Short wheel tricks at night are to be aimed at certainly, as the dozy man struggling to stay awake will steer a course like a wallpaper pattern. Dark nights make it harder to resist sleep. The binnacle with a rheostat control is an invaluable help. The binnacle which throws a blinding shaft of light skywards will not only ruin the man's night-sight, but hypnotize him into a nightmare doze. I have dozed over the wheel and awakened by clipping myself with the spokes and all because of such a light. It has the effect of drawing you into it so that, after an hour of it, nothing seems to exist save that great grinning full moon of a card and the rush of wind and water out of the surrounding blackness.

If you find yourself falling asleep, say so. And if you're racing, get off the wheel—as long as there is someone else to take her. Get your watch-mate to yarn to you if you aren't racing, but keep those voices low, as sound from the cockpit carries straight below and no matter how philosophical the subject (and it always is) the gang below listening and grating their teeth won't be pleased.

Have plenty for the night watches to do. An hourly deck log entry, regular sail, lights and chafe check-ups, all this gives the watch a purpose and defeats that hen-roost crouch, this biscuit-munching apathy, that glucose-sucking gloom or perhaps an attack of the howling nadgers, said to be fatal.

There should be a perpetual brew for the night crowd. The old sailing trawlers used to have a tea-kettle which simmered on the stove from beginning to end of a trip, maybe lasting weeks. Fresh tea and treacle went in at regular intervals and all could refresh (sic) themselves when inclined. Nowadays a big pan of cocoa—really big—is a good plan.

The next watch should be roused with ten minutes to go. It's no kindness to let them sleep it out and call them on the nail unless you are happy to stay on over your time to let them get ready. The man who has to dance blasphemously around a gyrating saloon trying to get into his oilies and sup cocoa with a minute to go is not a pleased man. It goes without saying that you should never, never, never be late on watch.

The night seems to breed a whole host of little meannesses in people. Who puts the dirty mugs out of sight behind the companion door? Who borrows your oily pants and doesn't take them off when he turns in—or readjusts the braces and leaves you to alter them back? Who pretends to mess about making tea for an hour when it's raining up top? 'All right on the wheel for a few minutes?' he says. Who stands on the top step of the companionway for three parts of the watch? Who overhears a whisper about changing head-sails and gently takes over the wheel? Who fumbles secretly with his private store of sweets when all the rest have gone or fills his pockets with raisins from the galley? Who was sick on the jib sheets in the dark and said nothing . . .?

Keeping warm is one big worry. It isn't a question of wearing more and more, but of keeping something in reserve such as a set of long woolly underpants or a duffle. Jeans are useless wear for the night watches, by the way. Don't put on full armour as soon as the sun goes in. It's best to put up with the bother of struggling into the extra stuff a bit later on when you *begin* to think you'll need it. Don't, by the same token, wait until you are chilled through.

When you turn in, take off as much as the state of the weather, possible emergencies, and size of crew make feasible.

The small cruiser with her crew depleted by seasickness, may find that dear old dad has to do a Roman soldier act at the wheel for half the night. By the time he is bug-eyed and flaked out, the ship can no longer be said to be safely under command. You could hit him with the Eddystone and he would only raise his cap. It is for the good skipper to see such moments in advance and either haul his jib a'weather so that he can doze a little with a survivor from below on steamer watch or he should keep to day sails until he is sure of an adequate crew. He should at all costs put a rope around his waist if he begins to doze, and that goes for us all.

Bunks should at all costs be comfortable and deep. Even small yachts today are fitting deep, pilot-type bunks in preference to the racks, shelves, tight-ropes and so on in which we have spent so many hours of ill-balanced nightmare. The owner who fails to provide at least two good safe berths so that his gang can get rest, hot-berth fashion in bad weather, is asking for it.

There is a tale about an owner who fitted extra pipecots up under the deck-head with about ten inches clearance. To demonstrate to his mutinous crew just how comfortable these were, he turned in in one. The lads had it all worked out. They got a nice splinterable kipper box and placed it on deck just above his ear; then they started:

'She's coming straight for us!' one yelled.

'Look out, look out.'

Then operator number three leaped on the kipper box, producing a terrible grinding, splintering crash. The owner sat up with a terrible cry and knocked himself cold.

THE £200 MILLIONAIRE

Weston Martyr

All that is necessary for the triumph of evil
is for good men to do nothing.

Edmund Burke

Smith versus Lichtensteiger

Smith stood 5 feet 5 inches in his boots, weighed nearly 10 stone
in his winter clothes and an overcoat, and he had a flat chest and a
round stomach. Smith was a clerk in a small branch bank in East
Anglia; he was not an athlete or a fighting man, although he
followed the fortunes of a professional football team in the newspa-
pers with great interest, and he had fought for a year in France
without ever seeing his enemy or achieving a closer proximity to
him than one hundred and twenty yards. When a piece of shrapnel
reduced his fighting efficiency by abolishing the biceps of one arm,
Smith departed from the field of battle and (as he himself would
certainly have put in) 'in due course' returned to his branch bank.

For forty-nine weeks each year Smith laboured faithfully at his
desk. In his free hours during the winter he read Joseph Conrad,
Stevenson and E. F. Knight, and he did hardly anything else. But
every year in early April Smith suddenly came to life. For he was a
yachtsman, and he owned a tiny yacht which he called the *Kate* and
loved with a great love. The spring evenings he spent fitting out,
painting and fussing over his boat. Thereafter, as early as possible
every Saturday afternoon, he set sail and cruised alone amongst the
tides and sandbanks of the Thames Estuary, returning again as late

as possible on Sunday night. And every summer, when his three weeks' holiday came round, Smith and his *Kate* would sail away from East Anglia together and voyage afar. One year Smith cruised to Falmouth in the West Country, and he likes to boast about that cruise still. Once he set out for Cherbourg, which is a port in foreign parts; but that time, thanks to a westerly gale, he got no farther than Dover. The year Smith encountered Lichtensteiger he had sailed as far east as Flushing, and he was on his way back when a spell of bad weather and head winds drove him into Ostend and detained him there three days.

Lichtensteiger was also detained at Ostend; but not by the weather. Lichtensteiger had come from Alexandria, with a rubber tube stuffed full of morphine wound round his waist next his skin, and he was anxious to get to London as quickly as he could. He had already been as far as Dover, but there a Customs official (who had suspicions but no proof) whispered to a friend in the Immigration Department, and Lichtensteiger found himself debarred as an 'undesirable alien' from entering the United Kingdom. He had therefore returned to Ostend in the steamer in which he had left that place.

Lichtensteiger stood 6 feet 1 inch in his socks, weighed 14 stone stripped, and he had a round chest and a flat stomach. He was as strong as a gorilla, as quick in action as a mongoose, and he had never done an honest day's work in his life. There is reason to believe that Lichtensteiger was a Swiss, as he spoke Switzer Deutsch, which is something only a German-Swiss can do. His nationality, however, is by no means certain, because he looked like a Lombard, carried Rumanian and Austrian passports, and in addition to the various dialects used in those two countries, he spoke French like a Marseillais, German like a Württemberger, and English like a native of the lower west-side of New York.

When Smith, and Lichtensteiger first set eyes on each other, Smith was sitting in the *Kate*'s tiny cockpit, smoking his pipe and worrying about the weather. For Smith's holiday was nearly over; he was due at his bank again in three days, and he knew he could not hope to sail back while the strong northwesterly wind continued to blow straight from East Anglia towards Belgium. Said Smith to himself, 'Hang it! I've got to sail tomorrow or get into a nasty fix. And if only I had two sound arms I *would* sail tomorrow and change it; but a hundred-mile beat to wind'ard and all by myself is going to be no joke. What I need is another man to help me; but there isn't an earthly hope of getting hold of anyone in this filthy hole.'

Lichtensteiger was walking along the quay. He glanced at the *Kate* and her owner with a disdainful eye and passed on, because neither the boat nor the man held any interest for him. But in Lichtensteiger's card-index-like mind, in which he filed without conscious effort most of the things he heard and saw, there here registered three impressions and one deduction: 'A yacht. The British flag. An Englishman. A fool.' Having filed these particulars, Lichtensteiger's mind was about to pass on to the problem of how to get Lichtensteiger to London, when an idea flashed like a blaze of light into his consciousness. To translate Lichtensteiger's multi-lingual thoughts is difficult; a free rendering of them must suffice. Said Lichtensteiger to himself, 'Thunder and lightning. Species of a goose. You poor fish. Of course. It is *that*! If *you* had a yacht—if *you* were a sailor—*there* is the obvious solution. Then there no more need would be to risk placing oneself in the talons of the sacred bureaucrats of Customs or within the despicable jurisdiction of blood-sucking and immigration officials. Why, say! If I had a little boat I guess I wouldn't worry myself about smuggling my dope through no Dovers and suchlike places. With a boat of my own then veritably would I be a smuggler classical and complete. But what's the use! I ain't got no boat and I ain't no sailor. But hold! Attention! The English yacht. That fool Englishman. There are possibilities in that direction there. Yes. I guess I go back and take another look at that guy.'

Lichtensteiger's second survey of Smith was detailed and thorough, and it confirmed his previous judgment. 'Easy meat,' said Lichtensteiger to himself, and then, aloud, 'Evening, stranger. Pardon me, but I see you're British, and I guess it'll sound good to

101

me to hear someone talk like a Christian for a change. I'm from Noo York, and Otis T. Merritt's my name. I'm over this side on vacation; but I'll tell you the truth, I don't cotton to these darned Dagoes and Squareheads here, not at all. So I reckon to catch the next boat across to your good country, mister, and spend the balance of my trip there with white men. That's a peach of a little yacht you got. I'll say she certainly is. She's a pippin, and I guess you have a number one first-class time sailing around in her. It's just the kind of game I've always had in mind to try for myself. It 'ud suit me down to the ground, I reckon. If you've no objections I'll step aboard. I'd sure like to look her over. Where are you sailing to next after here?'

'Harwich,' answered Smith. 'Come aboard and look round if you like by all means; but I'm afraid you won't find very much to see here.'

'Why, she's the finest little ship I ever set eyes on,' cried Lichtensteiger a few minutes later, settling himself on the cabin settee. 'And to think you run her all alone. My gracious! Have a cigar?'

'Thanks,' said Smith. 'I do sail her by myself usually, but this time I'm afraid I've bitten off more than I can chew. You see, I've got to get back to Harwich within three days. If I had another man to help me I'd do it easily, but with this wind blowing it's a bit more than I care to tackle alone.'

After that, of course, it was easy for Lichtensteiger. He did not ask Smith if he could sail with him; he led Smith on to make that suggestion himself. Then he hesitated awhile at the unexpectedness of the proposal, and when he finally yielded to persuasion, he left Smith with the impression that he was doing him a favour. It was very beautifully done.

That night Lichtensteiger transferred himself and two suitcases from his hotel and slept aboard the *Kate*. At daybreak next morning they sailed. Once outside the harbour entrance Smith found the wind had fallen to a moderate breeze, but it still blew out of the north-east, making the shaping of a direct course to Harwich impossible. Smith, therefore, did the best he could. He put the *Kate* on the starboard tack and sailed her to the westward along the Belgian coast.

It did not take Smith long to discover that Lichtensteiger was no sailor. He could not steer or even make fast a rope securely. In half an hour it became clear to Smith that Lichtensteiger literally did not know one end of the boat from the other, and within an hour he realised that his passenger, instead of helping him, was going to be a hindrance and an infernal nuisance as well. Lichtensteiger did all those things which must on no account be done if life is to be made livable in the confined space aboard a small boat. In addition to other crimes, Lichtensteiger grumbled at the motion, the hardness of the bunks and the lack of head-room in the cabin. He left his clothes scattered all over the yacht, he used the deck as a spittoon, and he sprawled at ease in the cockpit, so that every time Smith had to move in a hurry he tripped over Lichtensteiger's legs. By mid-day Smith had had as much of Lichtensteiger's company as he felt he could stand. Now that the weather was fine and looked like remaining so, he knew he could easily sail the *Kate* home by himself. He said, 'Look here, Merritt; I'm afraid you don't find yachting in such a small boat is as much fun as you thought it was going to be. See those buildings sticking up on the shore there? Well, that's Dunkerque, and I'll sail in and land you, and then you can catch the night boat over to Tilbury nice and comfortably. I'll run you in there in half an hour.'

Smith's suggestion astounded Lichtensteiger, and produced in him so profound an alarm that he forgot for a moment that he was Merritt. His eyes blazed, the colour vanished from his face, and tiny beads of sweat hopped out upon it. Then Lichtensteiger emitted some most extraordinary sounds which, had Smith but known it, were Switzer-Deutsch curses of a horrid and disgusting kind, coupled with an emphatic and blasphemous assertion that nothing, not even ten thousand flaming blue devils, could force him to set foot upon the suppurating soil of France. In fairness to Lichtensteiger it must be stated that he very rarely forgot himself, or any part he might happen to be playing, and it was also always difficult to frighten him. But the toughest ruffian may be, perhaps, excused if he shrinks from venturing into a country which he has betrayed in time of war. And this is what Lichtensteiger had done to France, or, more precisely, he had twice double-crossed the French Army Intelligence Department, Section Counter-Espionage, Sub-section N.C.D. And the penalty for doing this, as Lichtensteiger well knew, is death. Since 1916, when Lichtensteiger succeeded in escaping from that country by the skin of his teeth, France was a place which he had taken the most sedulous pains to avoid, and at the sudden prospect of being landed there he lost his grip of himself for fifteen seconds. Then he pulled himself together and grinned at Smith and said, 'Dunkerque nix! Nothing doing. I guess not. And don't you make any mistake, brother; I think this yachting stuff's just great. I'm getting a whale of a kick out of it. So we'll keep on a-going for Harwich. Sure, we will. You bet. And no Dunkerque. No, sir. No Dunkerque for mine. Forget it.'

Smith said, 'Oh! All right,' and that was all he said. But he was thinking hard. He thought, 'Be God! That was queer. That—was—*damned* queer. The fellow was scared to death. Yes—to *death*! For I'll swear nothing else could make a man look like that so suddenly. He turned absolutely green. And he sweated. And his eyes—He was terrified. And he yammered, panicked, babbled—in German, too, by the sound of it. By gosh! I wonder who he is? *And what it is he's been up to?* Something damnable, by the look of it. And whatever it was, he did it in Dunkerque—or in France, anyway. That's plain. To look like that at the mere thought of landing in France! My God, he might be a murderer, or anything. Cleared out into Belgium and hanging about, waiting his chance to get away probably. And here I am, helping him to escape. Oh Lord, what a fool I was to let him come! I actually *asked* him to come. Or did I? Yes, I did; but it seems to me now, with *this* to open my eyes, that he meant to come all the time. He did! He led me on to ask him. I can see it all now. He's a clever crafty devil—and he's twice my size! Oh, hang it all. This is *nasty*.'

Smith was so absorbed by his thoughts that he did not notice the change of wind coming. The *Kate* heeled suddenly to the puff, her sheets strained and creaked, and she began to string a wake of bubbles and foam behind her. 'Hullo,' said Smith, 'wind's shifted and come more out of the north. We'll be able to lay our course a little better now; she's heading up as high as nor'-west. I'll just see where that course takes us to if you'll bring up the chart.'

Lichtensteiger brought the chart from the cabin table, and Smith spread it out upon the deck. 'Not so good,' said he, after gazing at it for a while. 'We can't fetch within forty miles of Harwich on this tack. A nor'-west course only just clears the Goodwins and the North Foreland. Look.'

'Then why don't you point the boat straight for Harwich,' said Lichtensteiger, 'instead of going 'way off to the left like that?'

'Because this isn't a steamer, and we can't sail against the wind. But we'll get to Harwich all right, although if this wind holds we won't be there before tomorrow night.'

'Tomorrow night,' said Lichtensteiger. 'Well, that suits me. What sort of a kind of a place is this Harwich, anyway? Walk ashore there, I suppose, as soon as we get in, without any messing about?'

'Oh yes. But we'll have to wait till the morning probably, for the Customs to come off and pass us.'

'Customs!' said Lichtensteiger. 'Customs! I thought—you'd think, in a one-hole drop like Harwich, there wouldn't be no Customs and all that stuff. And, anyways, you don't mean to tell me the Customs'll worry about a little bit of a boat like this?'

'Oh yes, they will,' Smith answered. 'Harwich isn't the hole you seem to think it is. It's a big port. We're arriving from foreign parts, and if we went ashore before the Customs and harbourmaster and so on passed us there'd be the very devil of a row.'

'Well, crying out loud!' said Lichtensteiger. 'What a hell of a country. Not that the blamed Customs worry me any; but—well, what about all this Free Trade racket you Britishers blow about? Seems to me, with your damned Customs and immigration sharks and passports an' God knows what all, you've got Great Britain tied up a blame sight tighter than the United States.' Saying which, Lichtensteiger spat viciously upon the deck and went below to think things over.

Before Lichtensteiger finished his thinking the sun had set, and when he came on deck again, with his plan of action decided upon, it was night. Said he, 'Gee! It's black. Say, how d'you know where you're going to when you can't see? And where the hell are we now, anyway?'

'A mile or so nor'-west of the Sandettie Bank.'

'That don't mean nothing to me. Where is this Sandettie place?'

'It's about twenty miles from Ramsgate one way and eighteen from Calais the other.'

'Twenty miles from Ramsgate?' said Lichtensteiger. 'Well, listen here, brother. I guess I've kind of weakened on this Harwich idea. It's too far, and it's going to take too long getting there. And I find this yachting game ain't all it's cracked up to be by a long sight. To tell you the truth, without any more flim-flam, I'm fed right up to the gills with this, and the sooner you get me ashore and out of it the better. See? Twenty miles ain't far, and I reckon Ramsgate, or anywhere around that way, will do me fine. Get me? Now you point her for Ramsgate right away and let's get a move on.'

'But, I say—look here!' protested Smith. 'I don't want to go to Ramsgate. I mean, I've got to get back to Harwich by tomorrow night, and if we put in to Ramsgate, I'll lose hours and hours. We can't get there till after midnight, and you won't be able to land before daylight at the very earliest, because the Customs won't pass us till then. And—'

'Oh hell!' broke in Lichtensteiger. 'Customs at Ramsgate, too, are there? Well, say, that's all right. I'll tell you what we'll do. We won't trouble no flaming Customs—and save time that way. You land me on the beach, somewheres outside the town, where it's quiet and there's no one likely to be around. I'll be all right then. I'll hump my suitcases into this Ramsgate place and catch the first train to London in the morning. That'll suit me down to the ground.'

'But, look here! I can't do that,' said Smith.

'What d'you mean, you can't? You can. What's stopping you?'

'Well, if you will have it, Merritt,' answered Smith, 'I'll tell you straight, I don't like being a party to landing a man—any man— in the way you want me to. It's illegal. I might get into trouble over it, and I can't afford to get into trouble. If they heard in the bank I'd lose my job, I'd be ruined. I'm sorry, but I can't risk it. Why, if we got caught they might put us in prison!'

'Caught! You poor fish,' said Lichtensteiger. 'How can you get caught! All you've got to do is to put me ashore in the dark in that little boat we're pulling behind us, and then you vamoose and go to Harwich—or Hell if you like. I'll be damned if I care. And you can take it from me, now, brother, you've got to put me ashore whether you like it or not. And if you don't like it, I'm going to turn right here and make you. See? All this darned shinanyking makes me tried. I'm through with it and it's time you tumbled to who's boss here—you one-armed, mutt-faced, sawn-off little son of a b——— you. You steer this boat for Ramsage, *Now*, pronto, and land me like I said, or by Gor, I'll scrape that fool face off the front of your silly head and smear the rest of you all over the boat. So— jump to it! Let's see some action, quick!'

If Smith had not been born and bred in the midst of an habitually peaceful and law-abiding community, he might perhaps have understood that Lichtensteiger meant to do what he said. But Smith had never encountered a really *bad* and utterly unscrupulous human being in all his life before. In spite of the feeble imitations of the breed which he had seen inside the cinemas, Smith did not believe in such things as human wolves. It is even doubtful if Smith had ever envisaged himself as being involved in a fight which was not more or less governed by the marquis of Queens-berry's rules. It is a fact that Smith would never have dreamed of kicking a man when he was down or of hitting anyone below the belt, and he made the mistake of believing that Lichtensteiger

107

must, after all, be more or less like himself. Smith believed that Lichtensteiger's threats, though alarming, were not to be taken seriously. He therefore said, 'Here! I say! You can't say things like that, you know. This is my boat and I won't—'

But Smith did not get any further. Lichtensteiger interrupted him. He drove his heel with all his might into Smith's stomach, and Smith doubled up with a grunt and dropped on the cockpit floor. Lichtensteiger then kicked him in the back and the mouth, spat in his face and stamped on him. When Smith came to he heard Lichtensteiger saying, 'You'll be wise, my buck, to get on to the fact that I took pains, that time, not to hurt you. Next time, though, I reckon to beat you up good. So—cut out the grunting and all that sob-stuff and let's hear if you're going to do what I say. Let's hear from you. Or do you want another little dose? Pipe up, you—'

Smith vomited. When he could speak, he said, 'I can't—Ah, God! Don't kick me again. I'll do it. I'll do what you want. But— I can't—get up. Wait—and I'll do it—if I can. I think my back's broken.'

Smith lay still and gasped, until his breath and his wits returned to him. He explored his hurts with his fingers gingerly, and then he sat up and nursed his battered face in his hands. He was thinking. He was shocked and amazed at Lichtensteiger's strength and brutal ferocity, and he knew that, for the moment, he dare do nothing which might tempt Lichtensteiger to attack him again. Smith was sorely hurt and frightened, but he was not daunted. And deep down in the soul of that under-sized bank clerk there smouldered a resolute and desperate determination to have his revenge. Presently he said, 'Better now. But it hurts me to move. Bring up the chart from the cabin. I'll find out a quiet place to land you and see what course to steer.'

Lichtensteiger laughed. 'That's right, my son,' said he. 'Pity you din't see a light a bit sooner, and you'd have saved yourself a whole heap of grief.' He brought the chart and Smith studied it carefully for some minutes. Then he put his finger on the coast-line between

Deal and Ramsgate and said, 'There, that looks the best place. It's a stretch of open beach, with no houses shown anywhere near. It looks quiet and deserted enough on the chart. Look for yourself. Will that spot suit you?'

Lichtensteiger looked and grunted. He was no sailor, and that small chart of the southern half of the North sea did not convey very much to him. He said, 'Huh!' Guess that'll do. Nothing much doing around that way by the look of it. What's this black line running along here?'

'That's a road. I'll put you on the beach here, and you walk inland till you get to the road and then turn left. It's only two miles to Deal that way.'

'Let her go then,' said Lichtensteiger. 'The sooner you get me ashore the sooner you'll get quit of me, which ought to please you some, I guess. And watch your step! I reckon you know enough now not to try and put anything over on me; but, if you feel like playing any tricks—*look out*. If I have to start in on you again, my bucko, I'll tear you up in little bits.'

'I'll play no tricks,' replied Smith. 'How can I? For my own sake, I can't risk you being caught. You're making me do this against my will, but nobody will believe that if they catch me doing it. I promise to do my best to land you where no one will see you. It shouldn't be hard. In four or five hours we'll be close to the land, and you'll see the lights of Ramsgate on one side and Deal on the other. In between there oughtn't to be many lights showing, and we'll run close inshore where it's darkest and anchor. Then I'll row you ashore in the dinghy, and after that it'll be up to you.'

'Get on with it, then,' said Lichtensteiger, and Smith trimmed, the *Kate*'s sails to the northerly wind and settled down to steer the compass course he had decided on. The yacht slipped through the darkness with scarcely a sound. Smith steered and said nothing, while Lichtensteiger looked at the scattered lights of the shipping which dotted the blackness around him and was silent too.

At the end of an hour Lichtensteiger yawned and stretched

himself. 'Beats me,' he said, 'how in hell you can tell where you're going to.' And Smith said, 'It's easy enough, when you know how.'

At the end of the second hour Lichtensteiger said, 'Gee, this is slow. Deader'n mud. How long now before we get there?' And Smith replied, 'About three hours. Why don't you sleep? I'll wake you in time.'

Lichtensteiger said, 'Nothing doing. Don't you kid yourself. I'm keeping both eyes wide open, constant and regular. I've got 'em on you. Don't forget it either!'

Another hour went by before Lichtensteiger spoke again. He said, 'What's that light in front there? The bright one that keeps on going in and out.'

'Lighthouse,' said Smith. 'That's the South Foreland light, I'm steering for it. The lights of Deal will show up to the right of it presently, and then we'll pick out a dark patch of coast somewhere to the right of that again and I'll steer in for it.'

By 2 a.m. the land was close ahead, a low black line looming against the lesser blackness of the sky. 'Looks quiet enough here,' said Lichtensteiger. 'Just about right for our little job, I reckon. How about it?'

'Right,' said Smith, sounding overside with the lead-line. 'Four fathoms. We'll anchor here.' He ran the *Kate* into the wind, lowered the jib and let go his anchor with a rattle and a splash.

'Cut out that flaming racket,' hissed Lichtensteiger. 'Trying to give the show away, are you, or what? You watch your step, damn you.'

'You watch, yours,' said Smith, drawing the dinghy alongside. 'Get in carefully or you'll upset.'

'You get in first,' replied Lichtensteiger. 'Take hold of my two bags and then I'll get in after. And you want to take pains we don't upset. If we do, there'll be a nasty accident—to your neck! I guess I can wring it for you as quick under water as I can here. You watch out now and go slow. You haven't done with me yet, don't you kid yourself.'

'No, not yet,' said Smith. 'I'll put you on shore all right. I'll

110

promise that. It's all I can do under the circumstances; but, considering everything, I think it ought to be enough. I hope so, anyhow. Get in now and we'll go.'

Smith, rowed the dinghy towards the shore. Presently the boat grounded on the sound and Lichtensteiger jumped out. He looked around him for a while and listened intently; but, except for the sound of the little waves breaking and the distant lights of the town, there was nothing to be heard or seen. Then, 'All right,' said Lichtensteiger. And Smith said nothing. He pushed off from the beach and rowed away silently into the darkness.

Lichtensteiger laughed. He turned and walked inland with a suitcase in each hand. He felt the sand under his feet give way to shingle, the shingle to turf, and the turf to a hard road surface. Lichtensteiger laughed again. It amused him to think that the business of getting himself unnoticed into England should prove, after all, to be so ridiculously easy. He turned to the left and walked rapidly for half a mile before he came to a fork in the road and a signpost. It was too dark for him to see the sign; but he stacked his suitcases against the post and climbing on them struck a match. He read: 'Calais—1½.'

A NICE DAY AT WILLOW REACH

K. Humphrey Shakewell

One ship Sails East, one ship Sails West
By the self-same wind that blows.
But it isn't the gales but the set of the sails
Which determine the way she goes.

From Yachts and Yachting, November 2, 1962

'What one really needs to cut one down to size', said Haemish Brambles in his cerise dressing gown, touching his toes, 'is a weekend on the river. Interesting sailing. Specialised technique. Plenty of fast movements and none of your damned cleat up and sit down routine.'

He was at the height of his 'strength through joy' period, and it was a terrible time for suffering. As for being cut down to size I walk around in a trench as it is and my experience had prompted me to foster ominous premonitions of what these fast movements might entail. I had also read a book about the subject from which I had gleaned that this river sailing was all very chummy, and people kept bobbing up from their tea to shout—'Bravo Nigel!' to someone who had just won a race.

I had gained the impression of a frightening 'anyone for tennis' air about the performance into which I felt I could never integrate my lamentable lack of social graces. But Brambles had spoken and to the river we went.

I indulged in the panacea of wishful thinking as we drove through the leafy lanes. I pictured in my mind's eye the rivers of Renoir and Monet—serenity and dappled leaf shadow, parasols and crinolines in the punts and a languid hand, white and exquisite as Dresden china, proffering a *foie gras* sandwich to a passing swan.

'Do not despair, Shakewell,' I said to myself. 'All is not lost. Here we may find the new language we seek—the new purpose. We have worn badly of late have we not and become boorish? Our fingers are shredded by jam-cleats and the boom vang has beaten the Bejabers out of our thinning pate. We deserve the whisper of passing punts and buttered scones in the shade.'

I fell fast asleep, as is my wont on such drives, safe in the capable hands of Brambles—whom I could unflinchingly trust never to have an accident with his boat in tow. When I surfaced we were at the Willow Reach Sailing Club.

Prosper Lupin is Commodore there, or sailing secretary or something. E. Prosper Lupin is a great old mainstay of the International Hepplewhites and a close confidant of Mr U. Fox. Things are always good when he is around because he exudes an aura of gracious living and the world seems to have slowed down a little to allow him time to flex his limbs and raise his glass. His wife, Prunella, is also a great duck and belongs to that imperturbable band of lady helmsmen who sail in gardening gloves.

All this was going to be fun. Though the prospect initially had thrown me, Haemish was clearly right. A nice day among the water lilies was what we both needed. 'Fast movements' be damned, not a leaf stirred and the only movement in the air was a vortex of cavorting gnats in the shade of the alders. One did not kedge here I was told, because there was no current. If someone opened a lock or a sluice, or some such, upstream to create a temporary flow, then one held the stem of a reed between forefinger and thumb. How deliciously soporific, I thought, and allowed myself an extravagant yawn.

There was a lovely view of the club lawn from the starting line and I took in every detail. The peacock butterfly that fanned itself elegantly on the buddleia, the delicate flowers that bobbed to the weight of the questing bees, the gaily decorous, siesta hour lethargy of the scene.

Twenty minutes after the fluttering wads from the starting cannon had descended into *Stormcock*'s bilge, we were still enjoying

114

the same view from the same viewpoint and there were two of them because of the reflections. Even Haemish with his well-known nil wind routine had failed to move a boat's length though there was a small lady who clearly had greater influence in celestial circles and had proved it by sailing her boat unobtrusively round the first bend out of sight, propelled presumably by the power of concentrated thought. Hers, I remember, was an extremely quaint old Hepplewhite, upon the centre thwart of which had been screwed a bronze plaque proclaiming in three European languages that it was dangerous to lean out while the train was in motion.

'Damned if I know,' I said.

'Tsk, tsk,' replied Brambles.

A swan craned its head over the gunwale and snatched my Kit-Kat.

The next moment we were all jumping about steadying booms because the *Queen Mary* was passing three feet away, filled with fun and laughter and transistor radios. When she had gone, it took us a few minutes to collect up the toffee papers, cigarette ends and orange peel that had cascaded into the boat. The reflections settled again and there we were once more.

'Let's have some fast movement,' I wailed, with the hint of hysteria creeping into my voice.

'Let's have some specialised technique.'

There came at that moment a most extraordinary meteorological phenomenon—something to do with thermal bubbles was Prosper's later explanation. We experienced not a puff of wind so much as a clout and we alone were treated to the benefaction, the boats a foot or two away remaining quite literally unmoved. *Stormcock* for no apparent reason reared up and nearly buried her stemhead in a forward surge of immense power. Her convulsive movement was that of a half-starved swan that had just located a loaf in the sedges.

Brambles, whose faith in all things mortal had practically evaporated, was facing aft watching some holiday-makers playing cricket against their parked motor car. I was lying on my back watching the swifts snatching invisible insects out of a brassy

115

summer sky. Neither of us was remotely ready for it, neither saw where it came from or whither it went, but in that time we had travelled forty yards and the scene had entirely changed. There came a rending and a twanging and a snapping and the world went dark. I parted the leaves and saw Haemish's mystified face.

Strange Disneyesque noises continued to come from aloft and more and more verdure descended into the boat—willow and alder, lichens and dry twigs. The sun had gone and we were in a place of equatorial jungle shade, hemmed in with the smell of decay and wild water mint. I ducked under the boom and came face to face with a cow. Her nose was on the level of mine and she evaluated me with an even diagnostic stare, orbited by a whirling maelstrom of flies. Her tongue emerged and sensuously explored both nostrils. Then, with the air of the practical opportunist, she bared her teeth and settled down to gnaw *Stormcock*'s gunwale.

'Git out of it!' screamed Brambles, thumping her in the ribs with a clenched fist.

'We must be ashore,' I suggested.

'Git out of it!' he went on, this time reinforcing his fist with the bailer. The cow, who had been cooling her hocks in the rushes, found herself unable to move as speedily as Haemish would have liked and they became irritated with each other. This is a situation which we wholesomely primitive people fully understand, but the more sophisticated a human becomes, the further he places himself from the unsullied datum of nature, the wider the yawning chasm of misunderstanding between himself and the animal. The cow, therefore, extended her neck, unhurriedly worked her stomach and, with a rich, flute-like undertone, blew a green foam all over Haemish's shirt and withdrew.

'We must be ashore,' I tried again. 'Shall I get out and push?'

But we could not push because the mast was in the trees and Haemish was concerned for his racing flag and his jumpers. I looked helplessly out through the draped fronds of willow and there saw Prosper and Colin Whortleberry-Flax who appeared to be becalmed in the open water about ten yards away.

'Prosper,' I called, 'we are in the rough. What is the procedure now?'

'Your mast is caught in the willows,' he replied helpfully.

'Look, Humphrey,' whispered Brambles, in a voice loaded with menace, 'climb that bloody tree and free it.'

We still had a good lead when we emerged which only goes to show that those who believe one can not afford to make mistakes in a hot class, know nothing about destiny.

A motor launch passed, cursed us for being in her way and asked if we had bought the river. Haemish replied 'No', and went on to say that he was not presently disposed to make a bid and even suggested where it might be put. There was little milk of human kindness in Haemish just then. He was hot and florid and very angry.

All troubles must reach an end. From afar came the sweet sound of agitated leaves, the rustle of reed stems and with it the warm summer aroma of pollen and water meadows. *Stormcock* seemed to sniff the air like a stag and chuckled away across the water, rejoicing in the poetry of motion. Brambles, one eye nearly closed by the sting of a horse fly, made appreciative sounds. A second or two later we were flying. It was a breakneck dash over water, smooth as glass. To weather of us a reed bed stretched along the water's edge, and we sped up it about four feet from the stems, giving an illusion of speed out of all proportion with reality. The reed bed was not all reeds. Every so often, lurking in a cleavage like some distressed bittern, crouched a fisherman, his eyes glazed over with what could as easily be death as concentration, watching a float.

Sometimes one saw the tip of a rod or the little red quill float in time to swerve (the expression 'bear away' seems wholly inappropriate here). Once we saw neither and planed on with the screech of a reel sounding astern amid a welter of unprintable invective.

The wind slackened and we ghosted quietly for a while, taking one or two anglers by surprise, one of whom even happened to be 'baiting his swim' as we passed, so that the nonchalant toss of his hand exactly coincided with our passing and *Stormcock* was liberally sprinkled with maggots and bran.

We passed some twenty anglers up to the gybing mark, and then, of course, had to pass twenty on the way back—on the left this time. We came to the one whose hook was still in our centreboard, and he was still spreading the gospel. Personally I love fishermen because I admire patience in any form, but this one never loved us and backed up his verbal malice by jabbing Brambles in the rump with the handle of his landing net as we came past. Brambles in turn called him a bastard, which clearly underlines the importance of mutual understanding among the widely differing enthusiasts of the waterways.

Bang went the gun and someone jumped up and said—

'Bravo Nigel!'

We had certainly had some fast movements and some quite specialised technique too. Nigel's, however, had appeared to show perhaps a little more consistency and greater purpose.

'Lunch!' said Prosper.

'Yes. Gin and lunch,' seconded Prunella.

'Oh, goody,' said I.

'Just one thing, Humphrey,' said Prosper, with the air of one recommending Amplex to his best friend. 'You must put some shoes on for the dining room. This is Willow Reach.'

'But I have none,' I said, 'except my mustard sneakers, and they look soppy with shorts.'

Prosper led me silently through a door labelled 'Changing Room' and I was comforted to note that the universal effluvium affecting such places knows no barriers, and though essentially stronger in the presence of a salt-water background, can still be quite formidable inland.

Prosper kicked over a pile of fetid clothes in a corner and produced for me an anonymous pair of canvas plimsolls from which both the toes and the laces were missing and from which exuded the smell of a damp camel.

'Put these on,' he said, 'the Flag Officers insist upon dressing for luncheon.'

HOMEWARD IN A HURRICANE

A. E. Copping

A Whole Gale

'In which a well-conditioned man-o'-war could scarcely
bear a lower main topsail and a reefed foresail.'
'And in which the smacks are all in harbour, pray God!'
'And, ashore, there is considerable structural damage and
whole trees are being uprooted.'

From Yachts and Yachting, January 6, 1956

Away we went, not tarrying for fresh stores, for time was more
valuable than new bread, and what if the water cask were half
empty?

'Why,' exclaimed Gotty as, having curved out of Torbay, we
charged the open sea on a strong straight line, 'if the wind keeps
in the west'ard, and don't fall away too much, we oughter be in
Folkestin' the day arter termorrer. It blows wonderful steady—
reg'lar walkin' through the water she is. In by Wednesday mornin'
I shouldn't wonder. Yer see, she don't feel the punt now it's aboard.
Goes twice as easy, she does, not 'aving all that dead weight ter
pull. If the wind don't drop. That's all I'm afraid of.'

On that point he spoke Cole's thoughts and mine. Because
perfection seemed too good to last, we feared a diminution of zeal
on the part of the wind.

But these timorous misgivings proved without warrant. So far
from lessening, the aerial velocity increased. Our mast oftimes stood
at a considerable slant, and the sea came on board at the bow in
gurgling mounds of frothy unrest, then streamed down the deck
and escaped hissing through the scuppers. Some passed into the

119

hold, where, on going below to consult my chart, I found disconcerting patches of wetness on my books, my clothes, and my bed. But we were going home fast. And faster and faster.

Being well out in the Channel, we had no occasion to concern ourselves with navigation subtleties, and this was just as well, for the pilot did not feel quite himself. He was cold and wet, for one thing, and he was beginning to have a headache, for another.

When day faded, Portland was far astern, and we were south of the Anvil light. All the reefs were taken in. The weather showed no signs of abating its boisterousness.

The question of running for shelter to the Isle of Wight was raised, but only to be unanimously negatived. No one was more prompt than the poor pilot in resisting the suggestion. He now makes frank confession that he would joyfully have gone into harbour if only his swimming brain had been equal to the task of reading up the necessary particulars. The lesser evil was to continue sitting, damp and impassive, on the provision chest, dully wondering if the storm would ever cease.

At midnight he put forth a great effort, and bestirred himself to the extent of thrusting an inquisitive head into the open air. St. Catherine's light shone brightly in the north; and no sooner had he made that observation than about a quart of sea water leapt over the dinghy and smote him on the head, icy trickles running down his spine. Stung into a certain amount of life, he fumbled about until he found his lamp, with which, having succeeded in lighting it, he scrutinized his apartment, if haply he might find a dry spot on which to deposit himself. But, with moisture dripping everywhere, the place had rather the look of a grotto than a hold.

My bed was saturated, and a sheet of water was ebbing and flowing across the oilcloth. Boxes and my smaller belongings were passing harshly to and fro, in obedience to the rolling of the vessel. A special lurch deprived me of the support of a chest, and abrupt developments were associated with the extinction and loss of my lamp. Extricating myself from those difficulties, I once more protruded into the open air, just in time to receive about a bucketful of cold sea at the back of my neck.

In oilskins, sea-boots, and sou'westers, Gotty and Cole were encased against those sharp discomforts; my own wardrobe including nothing appropriate to a gale. But I submitted the less rebelliously to the disability on reflecting that my better-clad companions were doing all the work.

Another subject of my unspoken envy was the way in which, clutching at this and that, Cole succeeded, when occasion arose, in traversing the deck without suffering himself to be borne overboard. Fain would I accomplish a gymnastic expedition of the sort; for my inclination lay towards the cabin, which did not leak, and where a fire was burning. Ultimately, and with great circumspection, I essayed and achieved the feat, much as a monkey climbs a tree.

There was no comfort in the cabin. I put coal on the dying embers, and Gotty must have noted the augmented smoke, for Cole struggled to the hatchway, and bade me suffer the fire to die down. Before that could be, the *Betty* indulged in a shuddering spasm which emptied the grate on to the floor, besides working mischief (as the din attested) in our crockery locker.

Afterwards came many upheavals of the sort. Water dripped through the deck, and spray came down the hatchway like rain. I sat or squatted in several situations, but always the lawless lurching of my apartment threw me elsewhere. Lying embedded in a heap of sails, I finally found stable quarters, and I remained there, listening to the roar of wind and water, for many hours.

It was my opinion that the bawley would not founder. Getting into that cold water seemed a thing so pitifully distressing that, by a piece of sublime egotism, I could not believe I should be called upon to do it. And, indeed, physical discomforts apart, there is a sense in which I was, so to speak, enjoying myself. It was drama, bold and spacious. Above, below, and all round, Nature was in a passion—the same Nature which had ofttimes lulled me with

121

rosebuds, blue sky, and linnets. In weak moments, during that awful night, how I longed for the sight and feel of land—if it were only a little in a flower-pot.

At about ten o'clock I came half-way up the hatchway and looked about me. The moist world was tinted in degrees of grey. Swollen masses of water ran towards us in unending succession, and each on drawing near loomed down upon us; but it got underneath the *Betty*, and rolled her about, and hurried on its way. At certain angles of the pitching I saw Beachy Head. We were going home at a pace far outstripping our most hopeful anticipations.

Astern, there were my shipmates, figures of rigid endurance, Gotty still at the helm. At about noon, to get within earshot of them, I clambered across to the hold.

On the previous afternoon we noted a schooner putting back into Portland. Since then the Channel had seemed empty of sailing craft. But we saw many rolling steamers, bravely breasting the weather.

In the early evening we were being hurled towards Dungeness. Suddenly, to the confusion of the helmsman, land was blotted from sight as by a fog. Having been continuously drenched all day by spray, we did not readily recognize that now we were also in a torrent of rain.

On the other side of the headland we encountered our worst weather. The *Betty* only carried her mainsail, storm-reefed, and a small jib. Yet so nearly did she heel over that Gotty perceived the necessity of lowering the former. Tackling his urgent and difficult task with spirit, Cole soon had the gaff on deck. With only a little triangle of canvas over the bowsprit, the *Betty* flew across Dungeness Bay.

Would there be water in Folkestone Harbour? Gotty shouted in my ear that I must learn the time of the tide. Somehow I got to the cabin; and, to save me the hazard of a return journey, Cole came crawling to the hatchway for that vital information.

It wanted two hours to high water. With my head out of the cabin opening, I anxiously awaited Gotty's solution of the difficulty.

He gave the helm to Cole, and himself came forward and lowered our remaining sail. Then so considerable a volume of water rose from the side and descended upon me that I withdrew into shelter. The next minute our vessel received a blow that sounded like a clap of thunder; a tremor passed through her framework, and I heard an avalanche of water fall on deck.

Amid the howling of the gale, Gotty's agonized shout could not have reached Cole. But the wind carried it back to me, and also I heard the skipper fling himself back to the stern. The less expert hand had held the helm; and to ship two seas of that character in quick succession might have meant disaster. With our dinghy sprawling across the opening, we could not—as now I realized—batten down the hatchways. Cole was slaving at the pump, and, when I judged his strength to be spent, I clambered across and relieved him.

With bare rigging, for an hour and a half the *Betty* staggered in that raging sea. Impatient to the point of pain, with the wind assaulting all my senses, I lived through a long experience of swimming on and on, and still for ever on, in a lost equilibrium of air and water madly mingled. But at last (for the tide bore us towards the shore) I beheld the harbour lights—rigid stars of composure; comfortable reminders that, with good luck, we soon should pass from that quaking realm of boisterous upheaval, and return to the dear old solid land, where roads and kerbstones and houses remained obediently still.

Hoist by Cole, our jib stood against the might of the wind; and, all athrill, we ran for the entrance lights, the tiller in Gotty's tough grip. Then came the sudden relief of sheltered water, and the *Betty* at peace at last, glided among the multitude of moored luggers in Folkestone harbour. A lifetime had elapsed since we left Torquay—but a lifetime of only thirty-two hours.

Into the public bar of a little inn went Gotty and I—two haggard and dishevelled figures, dripping with salt water and rain. I think it was not the rum we met with, but the reception, that put warmth into my companion. That group of veteran fishermen, sociably assembled under shelter, broke into exclamations of honest astonishment when we went splashing into their midst.

'You've come through it, then!' cried one.

'So that little boat o' yourn,' observed another, with respectful eyebrows raised, 'can stand a bit o' weather!'

'Evenin',' replied Gotty, in friendly greeting to one and all; and not till he had swallowed the first dose of my prescription did he vouchsafe any relief to the curiosity our appearance had excited. Then he casually let fall one crisp, comprehensive sentence:

'We've jest run up from Torky.'

At these tidings the Folkestone men exchanged expressive glances; then bent their eyes anew on the pair of storm-stained mariners.

'Not sorry to be in harbour, I dessay?' one presently ventured.

'Not sorry!' cried Gotty, depositing his tumbler on a table, to be the better able to unlock the inmost chambers of his soul; 'not sorry! Look 'ere, mate! I wouldn't go through that lot again not fer a 'undred pound—nor yet two 'undred; there you are. I've seen a bit o' wind, and I've seen a bit o' weather, at our place sometimes; but talk about larst night! It wasn't water—it was boilin' froth, and all round yer the same! There was times when I thought she was goin' ter shut the door—that's the truth I did . . . "Where's the Guv'nor?" I says to Joe, fer I 'adn't set eyes on 'im all day. "Is 'e dead or alive?" I says. "'E was when I see 'im larst," says Joe. "Thank Gawd fer that," I says.'

Next day the storm was over; and on the evening tide we entered upon the last stage of our voyage.

Restored to his delighted family, Cole had exhibited a complacency that rather jarred on Gotty and the Guv'nor. So we scorned to ask his further assistance, particularly as we had no hope that he would concede it. We two took the *Betty* back.

Passing the Foreland next morning, I rolled up my chart. The pilot's work was done. We had re-entered the old familiar estuary—Gotty's world.

Four hours later, with Essex still invisible, I was aghast to feel our keel bumping submerged solidity. As Gotty seized an oar and plunged on both sides for the depth, his face was dark with agony.

'Clumsy old duffer!' I gasped.

'Oh, dear,' he whimpered. 'We ain't goin' ter be pulled up, are we? Shorely—shorely we ain't!' Suddenly his countenance brightened, and he shouted: 'Parst it! Bray'vo!'

'Yes, but—' I began, indignantly.

'I fancied,' he explained in excitement, 'there'd be a fadum over that bank. Not quite there wasn't. But jest enough. That's saved us five miles and charnse it.'

So I forgave him.

They saw us coming. Mrs Gotty stood waiting and waving on the jetty.

'Well, sir,' she exclaimed, as our dinghy touched the stairs, 'I hope he's been behaving himself.'

'Don't talk so silly!' said Gotty.

THE

URIST'S MAP

OF

COTLAND.

British Miles

5   10   15   20

EXPLANATION

Railways
Stage Coach and Mail Roads
Other Carriage Roads
Foot and Bridle Paths
Steamer Routes

A NIGHT IN THE TRESHNISH ISLES

Veritas

For the practise of witchcraft and sorcerie they (the Lapps)
passé all nations in the worlde. Though for enchanting of
ships that saile along their coast (as I have heard it reported)
and their giving of winds good to their friends, and contrary
to other whom they meane to hurt by tying of certaine knots
upon a rope somewhat like the tale of Aeolus hiswindbag) is
a very fable, devised (as may seem) by themselves to terrifie
sailers for coming neere their coast.

Master Giles Fletcher, The Russ Commonwealth.

From Clyde Cruising Club Journal, 1960

Last autumn my wife and I had a most curious experience and I am
recounting it now in the hopes that someone will offer a rational
explanation other than that the evidence has been faked or that we
were both very, very drunk.

We were having a late September 'last cruise of the year', and
had left Tobermory in the early afternoon intending to go to Iona
but, rounding Ardmore Point, we found not only the strongly
running flood against us but also, quite unexpectedly, a stiff south-
west breeze.

The result was that by the time it was coming on for the
darkening we were down only as far as about a mile north of the
Treshnish Isles. Here we decided to call it a day so, in the last of
the light and at near dead high water, we crept in through the
reefs and anchored in the little bight off Sgeir nan Caisteal. Quickly
we cleared up on deck and soon were sitting down to our supper.

Our meal finished we sat on for a while dallying over our coffee
and cigarettes and as we did so there was a slight bump alongside.

127

I jumped up on deck and found a small dinghy (more a coracle than a boat) lying on our starboard side. In it was a short, broad-shouldered man with a neat, sharp-pointed beard and wearing an ancient battered yachting cap.

'Good evening,' he said as soon as I appeared and I realised at once that he was an American, not a brash New Yorker but one of the softer-spoken lot—from Boston, say.

I returned his greeting and asked what I could do for him.

'I saw you come in,' he said and waved his hand in a north-easterly direction and, looking as he indicated, I saw the dim outline of a yacht and a bright riding light about a couple of hundred yards off. Even then I thought it curious that neither my wife nor I had seen it earlier as we must have passed quite close to it.

'I'm cruising single-handed,' the man continued then, musingly, 'been cruising a long, long, time and sometimes I get very lonely,' then, more briskly, 'and I would be real obliged if you would take pity on an old man and come across and have a yarn and cheer me up.'

'Of course,' I said. 'We'd love to. We've just finished supper and as soon as we are cleared up we'll be right along and be very glad to do so. But come aboard, now, for a minute and meet my wife.'

He scrambled, rather stiffly, aboard but I could see by the way he handled his painter and made it fast with a flick of the wrist that he was no novice in a boat. We went down into our cabin and my wife was introduced. Of course she had heard all that had been said and miraculously, the way wives do, she had managed to tidy up the cabin and bundle all the supper things out of sight.

When being introduced our visitor bowed in a quaint, rather old-fashioned way to my wife then went on to say he would hurry back to his boat to get ready for 'such a very charming guest'. The way he said this made it sound not the least bit insincere and I could see my wife was genuinely pleased.

'Before you go,' she cried, 'you must sign our book.' She took our Visitors Book down from the bookshelf, turned it to the right page, then handed it over together with a pen.

Laboriously the man signed then, before we had a chance to read what he had written, he shut the book and replaced it on the shelf.

Two minutes later he was off and I was hauling our dinghy alongside so that we could follow him.

'Did you catch his name?' whispered my wife.

'No, I didn't,' I replied, also in a whisper. 'He sort of mumbled it and the accent beat me.'

As we closed the old type, straight-stemmed, very high free-boarded yacht we saw our host-to-be was busy sweeping down his decks. He must have had them sanded because, as we drew alongside, several small stones rattled into our dinghy and, as it fell one hit my foot.

We got aboard and went down into the rather dimly lit cabin. I had hoped to get a better look at the man than I had had previously but, somehow, he always seemed to be in the shadows and all I could definitely say was that he was a lot older than I had first thought and I found myself wondering how he managed all alone at his age.

Soon we were grouped round his table drinking coffee and my wife and I were trying not to notice the astonishingly thick tobacco which he smoked in a meerschaum pipe (a thing neither my wife nor I had ever seen before—I thought they had died about the same time as King Edward VII).

He was almost pathetically glad of our company and kept repeating again and again, always in the same musing tone, how lonely he sometimes got always sailing and always alone. 'You know,' he said once, 'it's many, many . . .' he hesitated and I had a feeling he was going to have said 'years' but had managed to check himself. 'It's a very long time since I spoke to anyone, let alone a lady,' and again he gave his stiff little bow.

Gradually he thawed and as he did so he found his voice and, till long after midnight, he kept us enthralled with his tales. Tales of faraway harbours, of gales in the high latitudes, of sweating it out under a blazing sun for days of soul-destroying calm in the tropics. Of adventure in low dives and high places. Of love and of sudden violent death. In almost anyone else, I would have set down more than half of what he told us as 'line-shooting', but he carried such an air of truth about him and everything was told in such a plain, unvarnished, matter-of-fact way with no boastfulness, that we never for a moment doubted a word.

About two o'clock we went back on board our own boat and tumbled into our bunks.

Shortly before six, just as it was beginning to get light, we began to roll rather heavily so I went on deck to see that all was well. Naturally I looked to see how the other yacht was faring and was a little surprised to see that she had already sailed. To sail out of that anchorage single-handed in the dark was not a job I would have cared to do.

Then, like a blow on the face, I realised something more. Not only was there no yacht there but there never had been a yacht there! There could not possibly ever have been one there!

I did not know the anchorage except as a Sketch Plan in the Sailing Directions and nothing odd had struck me the night before but, in the daylight, it was all too clear to me that if a yacht had been anchored where the old man's had been it must have been high and dry on top of the islet lying to the north-east of us.

Bewildered, I called my wife to come up and join me so that I could see what her reactions would be.

Not very willingly she turned out and poked her head out of the hatch and she, too, looked to the north-east.

'Oh, he's gone already,' she said, then a look of puzzlement came over her face. 'But goodness! How . . .'

'Quite,' I interrupted. 'How? Why? Who? What?'

For a moment nothing was said then my wife laughed a little uncertainly. 'Of course,' she said, 'we must have been swinging the other way.'

'In that case,' I countered, 'he was anchored half-way up that hill on Lunga.'

My wife ducked down out of sight leaving me pondering and,

for some reason, vaguely uneasy. In a minute she re-appeared, and in her hand was the Visitors Book.

'This is more than queer, or it's a poor joke,' she said handing me the open book and I could see that besides being as bewildered as myself she was more than a little frightened.

I glanced quickly at the open page and there, written in an old-fashioned, copper plate writing, was the entry:

Joshua Slocum .... Spray.

'This is damned silly, altogether,' I thought, then, remembering the stone that had hit my foot the night before, I went aft, hauled our dinghy alongside and then, from underneath the floor boards, recovered half a dozen needle-pointed common tacks!

I have them in front of me as I write so they, at least, are facts that cannot be easily explained away. You will remember, if you have read his book, that at night Slocum always strewed his decks with just such tacks.

MAELSTROM

W. H. Murray

'Blow winds, and crack your cheeks! rage! blow!
William Shakespeare, King Lear

The Sound of Jura

Braid Hogan's flight line across Scotland used Lochs Tay and Awe for pointers. His passengers were too thankful for this long hop to feel the discomfort of a craft converted to the transport of fodder and chemicals. Aided by clear skies and perfect visibility, they had soon crossed the Scottish watershed beyond Tyndrum to enter a new weather system, marked by a strong westerly wind. It lost them time, despite which only one hour and a quarter had elapsed between their first speech with Hogan and their first sighting of Loch Craignish.

They saw it from the southern head of Loch Awe, a long blue fiord streaked by long green islands, and swung due west, losing height. Hogan had aimed to land on the flat fields at the sea-loch's head, alongside the main road, when Hamish, who was using Hogan's field-glasses to spy out the land, turned them on Ardfern.

'*Zak*'s away! She's gone! No ship there!'

'Give me them.' John almost snatched the glasses. He looked.

'McKechnie's failed to get out in time,' said Hamish grimly.

'Aye, she's sailed,' confirmed John. 'Mr Hogan, would you please run south down the loch?'

Hogan nodded. Holding his altitude of one thousand feet, he turned south to follow the green line of Eileen Righ, nearly two miles long.

133

Being in a better position, Hamish again took the glasses and at once spotted a glint of white sails to the west of the last island. He steadied the glasses. 'There's a ketch out on the loch,' he announced. 'Beating south for the entrance. A low sail for a long hull. Surely it can't be *Zak*?'

'Any stick will look short in this wind,' said John. 'A yacht will be well-heeled.'

Hamish passed him the glasses.

'Doesn't *seem* to be heeled,' John agreed ... 'Good God! She *is* Zak! They've hoisted main, mizzen, and staysail. That gin palace—sailing! But sail she must—or Strunk wouldn't try.'

'Then McKechnie's done his job?' cried Thea.

'By the lord Harry, he has!' swore John.

'Will I drop down and buzz her?' asked Hogan.

'No!' commanded John. 'Keep inland now. We don't want her warned.'

They turned leftward and down the line of low coastal hills, skimming over the tops, which rose to six hundred feet.

'Mr Hogan,' said Hamish, 'could you put us down at Crinan?'

'Aye, I suppose I could if there's flat ground. But what guid will that dae?'

'There's a ship we can use.' He turned to John and Thea. *Sula Sgeir*.

'If there's not a police guard on her,' said John.

'I still dinna see what you'll dae wi' the boat,' said Hogan flatly.

'Follow or attack,' replied Hamish. 'We're armed.'

'The answer is, follow,' advised John. 'One can't foresee what chance will offer, but we'd come off second best in a fight.'

'It may not be easy getting aboard *Sula*,' he continued. 'If she's in the Crinan basin the loch-keepers will be watching her for the police. Easier if she's at anchor in Crinan Loch, outside the canal.'

'Don't forget I'm the owner's daughter,' Thea reminded him. 'She had full tanks when we sailed from Ireland, and we never once used the engine. It's a fifty-horsepower diesel. It drives her at seven knots ... But how far and fast can *Zak* move under sail?'

'Far but not fast,' John shrugged. 'I don't know the ship. She'll be good under power. Under sail like an old cart-horse. Before this fresh breeze, she might run at three knots, but make only two and a half beating against it.'

In a few minutes they were soaring across Crinan Loch. They dropped to circle the canal's terminal basin and Crinan hotel. At the basin, two fishing smacks and a motor-cruiser were made fast to the quays, but no *Sula Sgeir*. They wheeled over the craggy knoll on which the hotel stands. 'There's good anchorage offshore,' remarked John, 'in two fathoms.' They could see an island there, the Eilean na Vain, and a yacht lying to moorings on its east side. She carried a tall stick. 'It's *Sula*!' cried Thea, adding disgustedly, 'They haven't even lowered the burgee.'

Hogan had been searching for a suitable landing point and seen one on the sands east of the canal. He returned there, and after much hovering 'ta mak' siccar', touched down. Hamish, John and Thea took time to shake Hogan by the hand and to promise payment for his petrol, but apart from that he never carried passengers who vanished more rapidly. They climbed up to the canal and ran along the towpath, down past the lock to the basin, then over the final sea-lock to the knoll above the shore. They could see now that *Sula*'s mainsail had not been stowed, but furled to the boom and covered. The wind stayed fresh to strong and the dinghy strained at the painter. They thought someone must be aboard, otherwise the dinghy would be stowed on deck. Scrutinizing her, they dropped to the beach. Hamish gave a shout, '*Sula* 'hoy!' but no answer came, nor to several repetitions. This was no time to stand on ceremony. A hundred yards along the beach a rowing-boat rode to a trip-line. They hurried over and hauled her ashore. John rowed them out.

Wind and tide were against him and gave him a hard pull. 'It's the second hour of the flood,' he grunted, eyeing the shore-marks. 'When *Zak*'s clear of Loch Craignish she'll make fast time through the Dorus Mor and the Sound of Luing up to the Pladda Light. That's why Strunk would sail, most like.'

'It still gives him a long weary beat to the Ross of Mull. Can't be less than thirty miles west of Pladda.'

'Aye, but the Ross is a long peninsula. If he made do with Loch Buie, at the near end, his final beat could be just ten miles—and what's six hours if he makes it? . . . If we can just be sure where he goes, we'll have done a good job.' John threw in this last remark, sensing and fearing in Hamish a tigerish intent to come to grips with Strunk. To his relief, no reaction came.

Sitting on the stern thwart, Hamish peered ahead, crouching, his face eager and lighted, his pale hair blown. Watching him from the bow, Thea had never seen such quickly expressive eyes, at one moment hooded and detached, then blazing blue in a keen attentiveness, or worried with a crinkle between. At last he said, 'She'll have a three-mile start on us.'

'Just the right distance. We'll hold her at that. With *Sula*'s dark green hull and no sail hoisted, we might escape notice.'

But Hamish's eyes were on Thea's hair, a haze of red-gold, shining in the sun.

'We have two pairs of binoculars in the saloon,' she said, 'if they weren't taken.'

They came alongside and scrambled up on deck. John went below at once to make a quick inspection. Hamish and Thea hauled *Sula*'s dinghy aboard and made it fast to the coach-house roof. John tested the fuel tanks. 'Still full,' he confirmed, and started up the engine. Hamish unlashed the tiller and Thea towed the rowing boat to the bows, secured the painter to the pick-up buoy on deck, and dropped the buoy between the thwarts. 'Get under way as soon as you like,' shouted John from below.

'Cast off!' cried Hamish.

Thea let go the mooring to port and they were away, heading out for the stark isles, which struck out like spurs into the Sound of Jura from the heel of Craignish peninsula. Like a blast of trumpets, the sun was blaring up the Sound, which already was in tumult from the whip of the wind, driving a million white horses across a tide in fierce flood. The universal agitation was at first bewildering—the rush, the dance, the dazzle, the spin of spray, the foaming tide between the islands—it hurt the eyes.

John climbed into the cockpit with binoculars, and for a moment studied the broad mouth of Loch Craignish. 'I've got her. She's right out of the loch. Entering the Dorus Mor.'

He took over the helm. 'Get the cover off the main and set her up, ready for hoisting—but leave tiers on. Then set the Genoa in stops. We might want them yet in a hurry.'

Hamish and Thea set to work, pulling out the foot of the main, inserting battens, then refurling and securing the sail again to the boom. They fetched up the Genoa through the fore-hatch, stretched it along the length of the deck, furled it like a tightly rolled umbrella, and fixed the furl with thread. They clipped the jib to the forestay, shackled on the halliard and hoisted, then ran out the jib sheets. Fast as they worked, they were kept busy until Rabbit Isle lay well astern and *Sula* was more than half way to Craignish Point. Immediately beyond Rabbit Isle there had come a sudden shift of wind from west to south-west. From the little and light cloud travelling fast overhead, they could see the prevailing wind to be still westerly, but the Sound of Jura was funnelling a local wind of its own.

Hamish picked up the binoculars. 'Hello!' he exclaimed. '*Zak*'s standing very far out between the islands.'

'What does that mean?' asked Thea.

'See these two islands?' answered John. 'They stand about a mile off the Craignish peninsula—Ris an Vic Faden and Ris an Tru. If you're sailing north you can choose one of two passages—up the channel between the mainland and these islands, or else between the islands to their outer side. Most ships take the outer passage. But in light airs, if a yacht has no engine, the inner passage is safer. The outer could be dangerous at full flood.'

'Why at the flood?' asked Thea.

'A branch of the flood sets straight across to the Gulf of Corrievreckan. If the wind falls light you'll then be in trouble—if you've no engine.'

'Strank doesn't seem to worry,' said Hamish. '*Zak*'s gone right through between the islands. She's taken the outer passage.'

'Oh, she'll be all right today. I wouldn't have done it myself, mark you. I'd stick inside if I'd no engine. I've learned that wind is a fickle mistress. But in a fresh wind like this I'd feel quite happy out there myself. She'll be safe out to mid-stream.'

'But why *should* she go outside?'

'Wind and tide. Strunk needs all he can get to drive that tub. He reckons to get more help outside. It might give him a longer reach before the true west wind hits him again. On the inner passage he'd be running before the wind, and maybe *Zak* goes faster reaching—or maybe Strunk just thinks so. It wouldn't surprise me a bit if that's the first time he's had sail on her.'

The *Sula* was fast overtaking *Zak*, closing her lead to one and a half miles by the time *Sula* entered the Dorus Mor. The tide was racing through the Great Gate at eight knots, bubbling and boiling, seething along the craggy fangs of Craignish Point, yet not halting the far-travelled under-swell, which smashed white across the rocks. Seized by the current and swept along, *Sula* rose and plunged like a horse hurdling, hitting a full fourteen knots. So exhilarated were the crew that *Sula* was through the strait and out into the Sound before they again noticed *Zak*.

'We're coming up on her too fast,' declared John. 'She can't be moving as she ought. Take the helm, Hamish. I want to watch.'

The roar of the Corrievreckan, like the distant thunder of guns laying down an artillery barrage, could be distinctly heard from more than four miles west.

John took a long look through the binoculars. 'She's gybed!' he exclaimed, 'all standing ... And again! ... No—curious—she's close-hauled, beating *northward* into the wind. Good Lord!—she's in irons, sails flapping like hell ... Seems to be paying off at the head now. She's sailing—starboard tack, wind north-east—north-east! ... God Almighty!—she heeled till I thought she'd capsize—never thought she had the draught and ballast to stand that much.

138

Another gybe! . . . And she's in irons again, all in a flap and falling astern! She must be a bloody chaos below deek!'

'But this is absolutely mad!' protested Hamish. 'We'd better mark time.' He put down the tiller and began to sail a wide circle.

'That kind of wind,' said John, 'is very common in the long narrow sea-lochs—always with a cross-wind overhead. The wind at sea-level then bears no relation to what's happening aloft. But it's rare out in the open—never lasts long, maybe half an hour or less. If you keep fighting, you win out.'

They had both binoculars on duty, and for several minutes were able to study *Zak*'s performance at leisure. She seemed to be holding her own, and if not gaining to northward, was at least not losing southward. 'I wonder if a north-going current can be aiding her?' speculated John. The two men had been hogging the binoculars, and thus it was left to Thea to make the fateful observation. 'She's getting smaller, dwindling.'

They put down the binoculars, and stared.

'You know, Thea's right,' said Hamish quietly. But John was looking at Thea, not *Zak*. She had paled, and her eyes had gone bleak. Before ever leaving the Mediterranean, she had heard her father talk of the Corrievreckan current and whirlpool, and had read the charts in the saloon.

'They've still a chance,' reckoned John. 'They may get a steady wind from the west in time . . . We have a decision to make. Do we go out after them?'

Silence.

'My opinion is,' he continued, 'that with this diesel, and with what help we can get from sail, we can go right to the mouth of the Corrievreckan and still win free.'

They looked again, using the binoculars.

'The wind has steadied,' cried Hamish. 'They're reaching—all sails drawing.'

'Aye,' said John. 'So they are. And they're in the race. It runs there at six knots. Look at that belt of breakers all round them.'

Half a mile to either side of *Zak*, they could see an angry white line. The thunder-roar from the Gulf seemed no longer distant, but came to them over the Sound with a boom of real menace.

'If we're going in, we'll have to go now,' stated John. 'It may not be necessary; yet if it is, later will be too late.'

'I vote we go in,' said Hamish.

Thea felt unable to look at them. She stared blankly out to the gaping strait between Scarba and Jura, narrowing from two miles wide at the outer lips to half a mile at the throat—that bellowing throat, in which so many ships had foundered in the twelve hundred years of its known history. She kept silent. The confusion of loves and loyalties was more than her mind could cope with in snap decision. She could not even judge the risk. And she had with her two men in whom her trust was absolute—in different ways. She held her tongue.

John's mind was clear. Approaching the Gulf the tide ran at six knots. When he tried to run out against it, he could expect seven knots out of *Sula*'s engine. Better still, he might expect eight knots from her sail if the wind held. Against her, though, would be the stopping-power of the steep seas—not a calculable force. In the Gulf itself, the race would be normally nine knots, but today, with the moon near full and a high westerly wind, the spring flood might well go through at ten knots in the throat of the strait, maybe more. In extreme emergency, he felt prepared to sail *Sula* to within two miles of the great whirlpool which formed at the farther end of the Gulf, but no farther.

'I will take the tiller,' said John.

He turned her bow to the Corrievreckan and sent her straight for *Zak*.

Once again Hamish observed in John that almost inhuman detachment he had noted on their first meeting. The eye alive but hard, in a man who long ago had been seized by emotional flood and swept off his life's course—into a maelstrom. The man who had survived—at a cost. Stripped of the common man's self-regard, he loved living and hard fighting, yet his paradoxical philosophy put no great account on his personal survival or that of others. It was such a man, thought Hamish, who could best take the decision now needed.

Hamish went below and fetched up three life-jackets. John gave a short laugh. 'You don't realize what the over-fall is like on a day like this. Jackets won't help you.' None the less, he put his on, as did they all.

'*Zak* is drifting a lot faster west,' said Thea, 'than she's sailing north.'

John watched *Zak* intently. 'She'll not clear the current in time, short of wrecking on the Scarba rocks. Her efforts to get north can only bring her closer to Scarba, where the current is worse than anywhere else in the Gulf.'

'What would you do in her position?' asked Thea.

'Accept the pull of the race but fight across to Jura. Had Strunk done it sooner, he'd have hope. He has none now. He lacks the sail-power.'

He uttered the last verdict on a sudden new appraisal. Judging time, distance, angles, his eye told him that *Zak* had passed the point of no return.

*

The Gulf of Corrievreckan

The wind still blew up the Sound of Jura, a false wind out of the south-west. Next moment *Sula Sgeir* was struck by a westerly gust, which veered rapidly north, blew hard enough to heel her under bare poles, then veered again east, slackening. There came a brief lull. Spindrift was swirling off the wave-tops to northward, its high dense spray shot through by rainbow tints as the sea-devil raced away, twirling up the Sound. Then the true wind renewed and blew steadily out of the west.

141

'We've passed the barrier that stopped *Zak*,' said John. 'The whirl has moved north. If so, we can use sail for a short spell—a close-haul on the port tack. It could save minutes.'

He waited. The west wind still held. 'Up main!' he cried.

Hamish and Thea leapt into action. Off tiers, free the sheet, a haul on the topping lift and away with the boom-crutch, then a swift hard haul on the main halliard. John secured the sheet. *Sula* heeled as the sail filled and a quiver ran through the whole ship. She seemed to leap forward, alive at last as she never was under engine-power alone. Spray sheeted across the bows.

Hamish and Thea scrambled below and donned oilskins. They brought up a suit to John, who struggled into it while Hamish held the tiller. *Zak*'s white sails, being low set, were now almost invisible amidst the lather of surf that spread across her sea. The seas were markedly steepening, and even *Sula* was pitching and throwing spray the length of her deck. It scudded on oilskins, stinging their eyes, yet gay in its flashing white had the Gulf not boomed behind. John again took the tiller.

'Out Jenny?' asked Thea.

'No time to handle it when we close in. In fact, the main will have to come down shortly. We'll be heading into the wind.'

Under sail, power, and tide, *Sula* was hitting high speeds, maybe twelve knots, thought John, until *Zak* lay off a bare half-mile on the port beam, still trying to claw out against the flood north-eastward, but now rolling horribly, her masts, short as they were, describing arcs in the sky that frightened even John. 'She's a more stable ship than I realized,' he conceded. 'But her only movement is westward.'

'Down main!' He turned *Sula* into the wind and wrenched in some of the mainsheet. Hamish and Thea let go and gathered in the sail, securing it with tiers to the boom, which they again set up on its crutch. Then they saw that Strunk had given up the fight. He had put up the helm and was trying to run before the wind straight to them. Inevitably, *Zak* drifted astern at much the same speed as before. Her sails, boomed far out to starboard, were a brake, no more. The gap between the two ships shrank to a couple of hundred yards. But the mile-wide race out in the Sound had been gradually narrowing; now concentrated to a half-mile belt, its strengthening current took firm grip of *Zak*'s hull. Slowly, inexorably, despite sail and rudder, it spun her round clockwise. She was out of all control. There seemed something terrible in that slow spin of the ship, as indicating that her fate and her crew's lives had been taken from man's control into the hands of the gods.

From *Sula*, three figures could be seen abaft the wheel-house, where there was a second wheel for navigation by sail. As *Zak* spun, the helmsman dropped the wheel and all sprang to the sheets. Too late. The wind had caught both main and mizzen aback. Quick as a wink, the booms slammed over to port. The main boom drove across with appalling force and took up hard on the backstay. It parted with a high-pitched twang. The ship rolled violently to the sea. Next moment the main-mast snapped like a matchstick and pitched over the side to starboard. *Zak*'s deck was an unholy clutter of sail and rigging. The crew reacted smartly. The mizzen first—sheet in and sail down. They looked like attacking the mess on deck when John, closing to forty yards, stopped them with a bellow. '*Zak* ahoy. Abandon ship. We come alongside.'

It was doubtful if they heard his words against the roar of water and wind, but they had no doubt of his intention and probably found it incredible. For they dropped everything. 'They're automatons—dazed,' muttered John. *Zak* had stopped spinning as she broached-to, for the clutter of gear over her side seemed to hold her broadside to the sea, bow to Scarba, and rolling. Hamish and Thea put out fenders to port, from the bow to just abaft the mast.

'*Sula*'s going to be damaged,' John warned Thea. 'I'll run her bow in among the wreckage to leeward. The ships will crack together on the roll.'

'Take the Menzies first,' warned Hamish. But there was still no sign of the Menzies. John brought *Sula* close astern of *Zak* and shouted, 'We'll take the Menzies first.'

Kirsten scramed back. 'We have no Menzies.'

'Where are they?' shouted Hamish.

'Blair Atholl.'

'A try-on!' hissed John. He stood up and shouted, 'Then drown and be damned!' and put up the helm. As *Sula*'s bow swung away, Macpherson shouted, 'They're here! They're here!' and pointed through the wheelhouse. *Sula* rolled, circled, and returned as John Menzies was brought on deck—dragged by Muriel and Macpherson, who each took an arm. Clearly he was unable to stand.

'My God!' cried John in anguish. 'My God! How are we going to do it?'

'We must hurry, hurry!' urged Thea. 'We must be inside the two-mile limit.'

Hamish could see the eastern promontory of Scarba lying astern and fast receding. Ahead stretched tumultuous seas, still recognizable as breaking waves until at a mile's distance a fearsome change occurred. A white welter of surf choked the Gulf from side to side, like the icefall of an Everest glacier. Already he wondered if John were not too optimistic in estimating escape. But John's eyes were like black stone and the jaw hard.

'Up to the bow—both of you!' he commanded. 'Tell them to prop Menzies up at the rail and topple him across when we touch. It's up to you to grab him.'

They scrambled forward. Hamish shouted directions to Strunk, who helped Macpherson to hold Menzies upright at the after rail. Never would Hamish and Thea have believed such a change possible in a man within three weeks. Menzies stood like a grey-skinned skeleton, slackly as if without sinew, the eyes inflamed with conjunctivitis, yet deep-sunk. He looked like a corpse exhumed from the grave, with the skin about to peel. John slid *Sula*'s bow close in to *Zak*'s stern, then with a skill and judgment that caught Hamish's breath, in one quick movement sidled the bow along the starboard quarter. The two ships rolled in opposite directions then thudded together on the fenders, splintering *Sula*'s gunwale. *Sula*'s deck lay lower than *Zak*'s, which made transfer easy.

144

Acting as one man, Strunk and Macpherson jumped the rail and landed on *Sula*, Strunk in Hamish's arms, Macpherson in Thea's. Mad with rage, Hamish tripped and threw Strunk on the heaving deck, and when he tried to rise, struck him down with a blow in the face. The two ships parted company. Menzies, left swaying at *Zak*'s rail, was saved from collapse overboard only by the ship's roll to weather, which threw him inboard. Macpherson sent Thea sprawling across the hatch-cover and turned upon John gun in hand.

John had seen what was coming. His gun was out. He fired thrice, but the ship's roll sent the bullets wide. Macpherson staggered aft to the upturned dinghy on the coachhouse roof, and fired. John collapsed across the well of the cockpit. Macpherson turned on Hamish, but fearing to hit Strunk, dared not fire and, remembering Kirsten, sprang instead to the tiller. Hamish wrenched up his oilskin jacket and drew his gun. Strunk grappled his leg, but Thea winded him with a kick in the stomach. Hamish reversed the gun and cracked the butt down on Strunk's head. He fell flat, blood trickling across the deck. Thea lifted the forehatch and jumped down, followed by Hamish.

Leaving Thea in the fo'c's'le, he hurried forward to the saloon. He would have Mapherson at his mercy through the companion way, he reckoned, even though he had closed its short twin doors. But Macpherson had anticipated, for Hamish found John's broad back slumped across the opening. He had been hit in the left shoulder and was conscious. He sat down with a gun at his head, neck propped by the hatch-cover.

Macpherson threw John's gun overboard and steered for *Zak*. Above the increasing uproar of the tide, Hamish heard a scuffling along the side deck, and, through a porthole under the coachhouse roof, glimpsed Strunk crawling aft to the cockpit, where he took the tiller and fairly screamed at Macpherson, 'Get for'ard. Help Kirsten.' Next moment the ships were pitching madly. Gouts of white water went rushing along the deck. Through the blurred portholes, Hamish saw to his horror nothing but surging yeasty seas, high and blinding white in the sun. They had entered the great overfall.

Strunk panicked. He pushed John aside and cried to Hamish, 'Come up! Come up!' It was no time to bargain—only one mile to go to the whirpool. Hamish gave Thea a shout and heaved himself up into the cockpit. No wonder Strunk had panicked! All around, the seas and tide were joined in the fury of battle. Armies of great waves driving relentlessly in from the west smashed on the spring flood as they would upon rock. Yet the tide was no passive rock, but it too a force unstoppable; thus they interpenetrated, and everywhere leapt high at each other's throats, madly clawing myriads. They burst in breakers ten feet high, spouting often to twenty with a crack like a pistol shot. *Zak* had again begun spinning, sail-wreckage and all, rolling and pitching. There was no longer a possibility of coming alongside. *Zak* was lost.

'Get out of my way!' Hamish spoke to Strunk, who obeyed with alacrity. He seized the tiller. His mouth tightened. 'We can't take *Zak* on tow. We haven't the power. She'll drag us. But we can check the spin and drift by throwing a warp, then get the crew off on a life-line . . . Strunk, make a warp fast to the mast, bring it aft, then for'ard to the bow round the backstay and shrouds.'

Thea, appearing now from below, dragged a warp out from under the counter. Strunk grabbed it and battled his way to the mast. He was sure-footed and worked fast, aft and then forward along the wildly heaving deck.

'Ready to hoist the main!'

Thea and Macpherson went to the mast halliard.

Aboard *Zak* Muriel had heard Strunk's shout, saw the coiled warp in his hands, and fought her way forward. Strunk clung to the forestay and waited.

'Hold it!' shouted Hamish, then, 'Up main!'

John heaved himself up, freed the mainsheet and knocked away the crutch. Macpherson and Thea hoisted. Up went the sail, nearly sixty feet overhead, flapping and cracking. Hamish had brought

146

Sula as near to *Zak* as he dared. Strunk waited for *Zak*'s bow to swing close in orbit, and threw the rope. It fell clean across the bows. In a trice Muriel had the end, skipped aft, and made fast to the mast. Thea and Hamish looked to the mainsheet while Hamish changed gear to neutral. *Zak* began pulling *Sula*'s stern to windward, the boom swung to starboard, and the main filled with a jerk. The ship shuddered and heeled. It was the wrong tack for the job, but that could not be helped now.

'Easy!' cried John. 'You'll part the warp!'

The long heavy rope wrenched taut but held. *Sula* came upright and Hamish engaged forward gear. 'Out Jenny!' Thea gave a sharp tug on the jib-sheet and the Genoa ripped open across the starboard bow like a cumulus cloud. Under sail and engine, the ship strained until the swift slide west gradually eased. Their only guide to movement was the shore-marks on Scarba. There was momentary silence in the cockpit as all watched. Thea fixed her eye on a big rocky claw abeam. They were dropping astern. For a moment *Sula* held steady as the wind gusted and the current lost grip, but the steep breaking seas gave her no chance, nor did *Zak*'s bulk, which allowed the current strong hold. Slowly but surely the ships fell astern. Already *Sula* was well-nigh unmanageable and her deck a-smother.

'Hopeless!' declared John. 'Give me the tiller.'

They propped him up on the seat. Blood from his shoulder was running across the back of his hand, but nothing could be done. Taking the tiller in his right-hand, he quickly sensed the ship's condition. 'No use. And she's over-canvased.' To Hamish: 'Take the life-belt, make it fast to a warp.' He kicked a coir rope from under the seat. 'Haul them aboard and cut the tow-rope.'

Hamish seized the life-belt off the counter and made the rope fast to it. He stood up, holding the yellow belt aloft, and signalled, shouting against the booming thunder of the overfall. Kirsten and Muriel came to *Zak*'s bow, Hamish dropped the belt astern and paid out fast. Kirsten picked up a boat-hook. As the belt bobbed past she hooked the rope. In a moment she had it up, pulled in the rope by hand, and slipped the belt over head and shoulders. Gripping it with her arms, she jumped.

Strunk, Macpherson, and Thea, all on their knees, had joined Hamish on the pitching counter and side-deck. In that welter of spouting breakers they never saw Kirsten again until her head emerged at the starboard quarter. They heaved her aboard and tumbled her into the cockpit, where she lay half-drowned and coughing up water.

Again Hamish paid out the belt. But Muriel was shouting at them from the bow. The wind was with her, and they caught the final words. 'John-is-too-weak . . . I stay.'

She repeated it. The belt was now below the bow, leaping and falling from pit to peak. Suddenly she stooped and grasped the boat-hook. In one quick, efficient move she hooked the rope and, hand-over-hand, hauled in the belt. To be sure they were aware, she held it high above her head as the bow reared, then deliberately cast it back into the sea. She turned her back and groped her way aft.

Hamish reported to John. 'She won't leave her husband. He can't make it. She won't let him die alone.'

Thea suddenly left the cockpit and scrambled below.

'We've a bare couple of minutes, then we're finished,' said John. 'I'll gybe the ship, and try to haul her out on the Jura side.' He knew this move must fail, yet as a last gesture felt not willing to leave it undone.

'Cut the cable!' screamed Strunk. 'Cut it now! We're not a mile off the whirlpool.'

The breakers astern had taken a more terrible aspect. They spouted fountains as high as *Zak*'s mast, the top part of which shone bright on blue sky, projecting out of a thick belt of spindrift. Her hull had vanished. Next moment *Sula* too engulfed. A continuous stream of heavy spray splashed on their backs.

'Ready to gybe!' commanded John. 'Get for'ard, Hamish. Make fast to a life-line.'

Hamish scrambled forward, ready to ease the Genoa round the shrouds and mast. For lack of any other life-line, he picked a long coil of the main halliard off the mast-cleat, tied a loop round his waist, and secured the standing end again to the cleat.

'Now,' said John to Strunk and Macpherson, 'get in that mainsheet fast—or we'll bust something on the gybe . . . Right—' Gently, he put up the tiller.

From the foredeck, and despite the slashing veil of spindrift, Hamish saw all too clearly how catastrophe ensued.

They let fly the jib-sheet. Standing at the topmast stay, Hamish gathered in the wildly flapping sail, then braced himself for the ship's heel. But John was taking the turn slowly. He now had *Sula* dead before the wind. Hamish seized the chance to bring the jib round the starboard shrouds. Macpherson sheeted in. Then they hauled in fast on the main-sheet till *Sula* was sailing by the lee. 'Gybe-oh!' cried John. He put the helm up. As the bow came round, the main boom swung over like a battering ram. Macpherson and Strunk had belayed the rope, and all was yet well. *Sula* heeled over on the new tack. Hamish clung to the lee shrouds, waiting for the ship to come upright as the cockpit crew eased off the mainsheet. Instead, Macpherson whipped out a sheath-knife and began to cut the tow-rope.

John let out a roar. He jumped to his feet and hacked Macpherson's shins, but Strunk hit him on the jaw. He collapsed backwards across the tiller, knocking it sharply to port. *Sula* rounded to the wind and heeled on her beam ends. Hamish was helpless. He had to cling for dear life to the shrouds, deck awash knee-deep. Next moment *Sula* leapt forward and was off like a charger into battle. She was fetching and quickly gathering speed down-strait on the starboard tack, powered by tide, sail, and engine, rails under. Strunk and Macpherson seized John and bundled him head first down the companion way. They unhooked the doors and shut them behind him.

Sula passed *Zak* to starboard. Hamish never even saw her across the uptilted deck and sheeting spray. But he saw the heavy tow-rope jerk taut across the rail and part like a thread. The most he could do was fight for a footing on deck. *Sula* was soaring over the seas like a bird, but knifing through the crests like a destroyer. Again and again water burst green over the bow, sweeping him thigh deep off his feet. His arms were exhausted. Breakers were towering high overhead. It could not go on. It may be that Strunk was scared of getting pooped. First he shut off the engine, and then, in one of the troughs, put down the tiller, presumably to bring *Sula* round to a broad reach. She was knocked flat on the turn. Next moment, Hamish tensed to a pang of fear. Above the almost vertical deck a great spouting breaker rose close to wind-ward. Its crest glittered in the sunny sky, like a vast, crystal chandelier. *Sula* rose to meet it, still sailing, when the crest broke abaft the mast. Tons of water thundered down upon the hull and deck. His arms were torn from the shrouds. He felt himself lifted over the rails, struggling, helpless under the invincible weight of water, at his waist intolerable strain, in his eyes, darkness.

His head burst out of the water. His hands closed on wire. The waist-loop had held, suspending him hard against the rail. The beam sea had rolled *Sula* upright. He dragged himself on deck and lay gasping. The first thing he saw was the dinghy, smashed to matchwood on the coachhouse roof, then the cockpit—empty. He unloosed his waist-loop and scrambled aft to the cockpit coaming. It was less than half full of water, scooped clean of crew. Long, hard and bright, Macpherson's knife rolled gently at the bottom. He and the Strunks had gone to the maelstrom.

The shut door of the companion way had saved *Sula* from filling, as too had the angle of heel. The water gurgled down through the grating, draining quickly into the bilges. Hamish flicked open the doors and looked down the companion way into Thea's face.

'We've been pooped. The Strunks and Mac are overboard . . . Press the starter, quick.'

The engine fired at once. *Sula's* stern had been spun windward. Twice the boom crashed over as the sail gybed and gybed again, but Hamish held her the second time as the ship gained way from her screw, and brought her round to the wind. Thea joined him and eased the sheets. *Sula* was now fetching, carried swiftly west by the tide but cutting across the race to the Jura side of the strait. She pitched and rolled through the steep breaking seas. The thunder of the overfall filled the Gulf. Shortly they were able to see the overfall, and across it to the hill-tops of Scarba. A wilder sight could not have been imagined. Above the chaos of raging sea raced a dense belt of flying spindrift, and above that again, a white fast-travelling fog where sheets of water torn off the sea were atomized. The big spouting breakers were astern, invisible now behind their own smoke. Abeam they glimpsed the dark bulk of a mid-strait island. It stuck out of the mad sea like a mountain-top out of cloud.

Hamish peered ahead, his face again eager and lighted. Thea saw a blaze of life in the blue eyes. 'The island's the crux,' he decided. 'If only we can work to the Jura side, we're through. The great whirlpool lies between it and the Scarba shore.'

They could hear John calling out below. Thea hurried down and found him kneeling at the companion ladder. She lent him a hand and he crawled up to the cockpit, grimacing from the pain in his shoulder. His forehead carried a new bruise from his tumble below, and his face was alarmingly pale—when one knew his normal, weatherbeaten tan. He stayed fully self-possessed. One quick glance round fixed his position. He scrutinized the sails. 'Ease out the mainsheet a few inches,' he commanded . . . 'Enough! Now the same with the jib . . . A little more . . . Stop!' *Sula* responded, heeling further, using still more of her hull at the overhangs, picking up speed. 'Fifteen knots over the ground,' declared John. 'If the wind holds, we'll have an outside chance.'

They could now see the site of the whirlpool. It lay five hundred yards abeam near the end of the Gulf, close in to the Scarba shore, which they could see to its north. Beyond it the Gulf widened to one and a half miles. There the seas were tumultuous, still in fierce conflict with the flood, but broke without spouting. The whirlpool looked not unlike a volcano, its crater spouting white water instead of red lava. The spouting ranged round a wide surging rim that rose and fell rhythmically, giving to its swift spin the aspect of inexorability, here sinking deep and there shooting thirty feet in the air—to be shredded by wind-blast.

'There's *Zak*!' cried Hamish.

Of one accord they stared at the maelstrom, *Zak* had appeared on the rim of the crater. All three sails had now been ripped off her. Poised on top of a high surge, she dropped broadside into the trough under a huge spouter, at the same time sliding inwards stern first to the suck of the whirlpool. The spouter crashed across her deck as she went, rolling her upside down. Next moment she had vanished, gone to the maelstrom's heart.

'Ease the sheets a little!' John barked the order at Thea, fearing she might break. He must keep her active. 'It's a quick, clean end. Better than most can hope for.'

Sula was now directly in line with the island, which had suddenly loomed up barely a couple of hundred yards ahead.

'Keep your nerve,' counselled John. 'Don't pinch her. She'll drift less as she is.'

'A hundred yards to go,' said Hamish grimly. 'We're not going to make it. Ready about!'

Before they could tack, a ferocious eddy swung them round to the Jura side. They were nearly scraping the barnacles off the rocks and held their breath lest they strike a submerged reef. Next moment they were clear. Before them the tide ran like a mill-race out to the broad Atlantic and to wide horizons, its white breakers less steep, even the roar of the great overfall receding astern.

When he saw that they had won through, John collapsed. Hamish held the ship on a westerly course, and when at last *Sula* drew away from the race he shut off the engine, lashed the helm, and helped Thea to get John below. They laid him on one of the settees and stripped off his oilskins and life-jacket. Using Macpherson's knife, Hamish cut away the sweater and shirt around the shoulder. The wound had stopped bleeding. But Thea dressed it while Hamish returned to the tiller. Then she lit the stove and made tea.

For two hours more he sailed a ten-mile circle far out between Jura and Scarba. His mind was a whirl of conflicting emotions. Heartfelt relief at escape with Thea and John—desolation at the death of her father and stepmother—the nightmare of struggle in the Gulf, the pooping of *Sula*, the tow-rope's snapping, the mad leap of spouting breakers, the drowning of the Strunks and Macpherson, and *Zak*'s wild fate at the maelstrom. The images were too vividly stamped to suffer immediate dismissal. He wondered for a moment what had happened at Eidart, but knew that Dougal and Donald would find little there save the blackened, empty shell of the house.

Thea brought him up a mug of hot tea. Her big hazel eyes were dark with weariness. For a short while she sat beside him in the cockpit, her head buried in his shoulder. He tried to lift his mind above her grief by remembering that the Strunks' defeat was the defeat of a Great Power's plan of aggression. On one side of the scale they had lost Menzies and his wife, on the other, saved millions, or at least won them a space of freedom and peace. It was a point of view that Hamish felt he could appreciate better than Thea. To her, the realities of this achievement must appear so many fine words. To her, the short truth was that she had lost her father and stepmother.

His arm tightened round her shoulder. 'Thea, my dear one, try not to dwell on what's done. It belongs to the past. Fix your mind on the days to be. Think of these and hold on to them. It's a time that comes to us all: we must look ahead and not back.' He kissed her forehead.

She whispered, 'Hamish, you are all I have.' And his heart lightened.

She went below then to look after Graham John. As *Sula* came in at last to Scarba, broad-reaching on a heavy swell, Hamish could see that the tide-race had almost died away. In a few minutes more it would be slack water. John was then sufficiently recovered to sit

153

up again and give counsel. Weak and shaken as he was, he had lost none of his tough resolve, and agreed that Hamish sail back through the Corrievreckan.

'You can do it,' he said, 'with a fair wind and tide and a sound engine. But you'll have only fifteen minutes of slack water to pass the whirlpool.'

It was not a course to be normally recommended. But they felt a need, if only for Thea's sake, to make a swift search of the Scarba shore. That there could be any survivors from the Gulf seemed impossible, save that at sea the freak chance always is possible. John crawled up to the cockpit to watch.

Hamish closed the Scarba rocks more than half a mile west of the whirlpool, *Sula* making nearly eight knots before the wind. The binoculars had survived on a quarter berth, and John and Thea used them to scan the rocks yard by yard. Abreast the whirlpool they could see a great cave, but the only moving things were black shags and cormorants, which lined the reefs in squads of twenty.

Hamish sighted the whirlpool two hundred yards off-shore. Its heart still showed a heavy pulse, but the rolling seas surged white in passing, not breaking heavily. He steered for the mid-way channel. The grey fangs and claws of that grim shore held no prey, alive or dead. Nor was there anywhere a vestige of wreckage.

John put down his binoculars. 'We sail for Crinan?'

Hamish nodded, and changed course for mid-Gulf.

TONO-BUNGAY

H.G. *Wells*

Twenty bridges from Tower to Kew –
(Twenty bridges or twenty-two) –
Wanted to know what the River knew,
For they were young, and the Thames was old
And this is the tale that River told: . . .

The River
Rudyard Kipling

Night and the Open Sea

Concurrently with writing the last chapter of this book I have been much engaged by the affairs of a new destroyer we have completed. It has been an oddly complementary alternation of occupations. Three weeks or so ago this novel had to be put aside in order that I might give all my time day and night to the fitting and finishing of the engines. Last Thursday *X2*, for so we call her, was done, and I took her down the Thames and went out nearly to Texel for a trial of speed.

It is curious how at times one's impressions will all fuse and run together into a sort of unity and become continuous with things that have hitherto been utterly alien and remote. That rush down the river became mysteriously connected with this book. As I passed down the Thames I seemed in a new and parallel manner to be passing all England in review. I saw it then as I had wanted my readers to see it. The thought came to me slowly as I picked my way through the Pool; it stood out clear as I went dreaming into the night out upon the wide North Sea . . .

It wasn't so much thinking at the time as a sort of photographic thought that came and grew clear. *X2* went ripping through the dirty oily waiter as scissors rip through canvas, and the front of my mind was all intent with getting her through under the bridges and in and out among the steamboats and barges and rowing-boats and piers. I lived with my hands and eyes hard ahead. I thought nothing then of any appearances but obstacles, but for all that the back of my mind took the photographic memory of it complete and vivid . . .

'This,' it came to me, 'is England. This is what I wanted to give in my book. This!'

We started in the late afternoon. We throbbed out of our yard above Hammersmith Bridge, fussed about for a moment, and headed down stream. We came at an easy rush down Craven Reach, past Fulham and Hurlingham, past the long stretches of muddy meadow and muddy suburb to Battersea and Chelsea, round the cape of tidy frontage that is Grosvenor Road and under Vauxhall Bridge, and Westminster opened before us. We cleared a string of coal barges, and there on the left in the October sunshine stood the Parliament houses and the flag was flying and Parliament was sitting . . .

I have thought much of that bright afternoon's panorama.

To run down the Thames so is to run one's hand over the pages in the book of England from end to end. One begins in Craven Reach and it is as if one were in the heart of old England. Behind us are Kew and Hampton Court with their memories of Kings and Cardinals, and one runs at first between Fulham's episcopal garden parties and Hurlingham's playground for the sporting instinct of our race. The whole effect is English. There is space, there are old trees and all the best qualities of the home-land in that upper reach. Putney, too, looks Anglican on a dwindling scale. And then for a stretch the newer developments slop over, one misses Blade-sover and there come first squalid stretches of mean homes right and left and then the dingy industrialism of the south side, and on the north bank the polite long front of nice houses, artistic, literary,

156

administrative people's residences, that stretches from Cheyne Walk nearly to Westminster and hides a wilderness of slums. What a long slow crescendo that is, mile after mile, with the houses crowding closelier, multiplying succession of church towers, the architectural moments, the successive bridges, until you come out into the second movement of the piece with Lambeth's old palace under your quarter and the houses of Parliament on your bow! Westminster Bridge is ahead of you then and through it you flash, and in a moment the round-faced clock tower cranes up to peer at you again and New Scotland Yard squares at you, a fat beef-eater of a policeman disguised miraculously as a Bastille.

For a stretch you have the essential London; you have Charing Cross railway station, heart of the world, and the Embankment on the north side with its new hotels overshadowing its Georgian and Victorian architecture, and mud, and great warehouses and factories, chimneys, shot towers, advertisements on the south. The northward skyline grows more intricate and pleasing, and more and more does one thank God for Wren. Somerset House is as picturesque as the civil war, one is reminded again of the original England, one feels in the fretted sky the quality of Restoration lace.

And then comes Aster's strong box and the lawyers' Inns . . .

(I had a passing memory of myself there, how once I had trudged, along the Embankment westward, weighing my uncle's offer of three hundred pounds a year . . .)

Through that central essential London reach I drove, and X2 bored her nose under the foam regardless of it all like a black hound going through reeds—on what trail even I who made her cannot tell.

And in this reach too, one first meets the seagulls and is reminded of the sea. Blackfriars one takes—just under these two bridges and just between them is the finest bridge moment in the world—and behold, soaring up, hanging in the sky over a rude tumult of warehouses, over a jostling conpetition of traders, irrelevantly beautiful and altogether remote, Saint Paul's! 'Of course!' one says, 'Saint Paul's!' It is the very figure of whatever fineness the old Anglican culture achieved, detached, a more dignified and chastened Saint Peter's, colder, greyer but still ornate, it has never been overthrown, never disavowed, only the tall warehouses and all the roar of traffic have forgotten it, everyone has forgotten it; the steam-ships, the barges, go heedlessly by regardless of it, intricacies of telephone wires and poles cut blackly into its thin mysteries and presently, when in a moment the traffic permits you and you look round for it, it has dissolved like a cloud into the grey blues of the London sky.

And then the traditional and ostensible England falls from you altogether. The third movement begins, the last great movement in the London symphony, in which the trim scheme of the old order is altogether dwarfed and swallowed up. Comes London Bridge, and the great warehouses tower up about you waving stupendous cranes, the gulls circle and scream in your ears, large ships lie among their lighters, and one is in the port of the world. Again and again in this book I have written of England as a feudal scheme overtaken by fatty degeneration and stupendous accidents of hypertrophy. For the last time I must strike that note as the memory of the dear neat little sunlit ancient Tower of London lying away in a gap among the warehouses comes back to me, that little accumulation of buildings so provincially pleasant and digni-fied, overshadowed by the vulgarest, most typical exploit of modern England, the sham Gothic casings to the ironwork of the Tower Bridge. That Tower Bridge is the very balance and confirmation of Westminster's dull pinnacles and tower. That sham Gothic bridge; in the very gates of our mother of change, the Sea!

But after that one is in a world of accident and nature. For the third part of the panorama of London is beyond all law, order and precedence, it is the seaport and the sea. One goes down the widening reaches through a monstrous variety of shipping, great steamers, great sailing-ships, trailing the flags of all the world, a monstrous confusion of lighters, witches' conferences of brown-sailed barges, wallowing tugs, a tumultuous crowding and jostling of cranes and spars, and wharves and stores, and assertive inscriptions. Huge vistas of dock open right and left of one, and here and there beyond and amidst it all are church towers, little patches of indescribably old-fashioned and worn-out houses, riverside pubs and the like, vestiges of townships that were long since torn to fragments and submerged in these new growths. And amidst it all no plan appears, no intention, no comprehensive desire. That is the very key of it all. Each day one feels that the pressure of commerce and traffic grew, grew insensibly monstrous, and first this man made a wharf and that erected a crane, and then this company set to work and then that, and so they jostled together to make this unassimilable enormity of traffic. Through it we dodged and drove, eager for the high seas.

I remember how I laughed aloud at the glimpse of the name of a London County Council steamboat that ran across me. *Caxton* it was called, and another was *Pepys* and another was *Shakespeare*. They seemed so wildly out of place, splashing about in that confusion. One wanted to take them out and wipe them and put them back in some English gentleman's library. Everything was alive about them, flashing, splashing, and passing, ships moving, tugs panting, hawsers taut, barges going down with me toiling at the sweeps, the water all a-swirl with the wash of shipping scaling into millions of little wavelets, curling and frothing under the whip of the unceasing wind. Past it all we drove. And at Greenwich to the south, you know, there stands a fine stone frontage where all the victories are recorded in a Painted Hall, and beside it is the 'Ship' where once upon a time those gentlemen of Westminster used to have an annual dinner—before the port of London got too much for them altogether. The old façade of the Hospital was just warming to the sunset as we went by, and after that, right and left, the river opened, the sense of the sea increased and prevailed reach after reach from Northfleet to the Nore.

And out you come at last with the sun behind you into the eastern sea. You speed up and tear the oily water louder and faster, sirroo, sirroo—swish—sirroo, and the hills of Kent—over which I once fled from the Christian teachings of Nicodemus Frapp—fall away on the right hand and Essex on the left. They fall away and vanish into blue haze; and the tall slow ships behind the tugs, scarce moving ships and wallowing sturdy tugs, are all wrought of wet gold as one goes frothing by. They stand out bound on strange missions of life and death, to the killing of men of unfamiliar lands. And now behind us is blue mystery and the phantom flash of unseen lights and presently even these are gone, and I and my destroyer tear out to the unknown across a great grey space. We tear into the great spaces of the future and the turbines fall to talking in unfamiliar to tongues. Out to the open we go, to windy freedom and trackless ways. Light after light goes down. England and the Kingdom, Britain and the Empire, the old prides and the old devotions, glide abeam, astern, sink down upon the horizon, pass—pass. The river passes—London passes, England passes . . .